Inspiration Tarot

A Workbook for Understanding and
Creating Your Own Tarot Deck

Inspiration Tarot

by
Gail Fairfield
and Patti Provo

SAMUEL WEISER, INC.
York Beach, Maine

First published in 1991 by
Samuel Weiser, Inc.
Box 612
York Beach, Maine 03910

Library of Congress Cataloging-in-Publication Data

Fairfield, Gail.
    Inspiration tarot : a workbook for understanding and
creating your own tarot deck / Gail Fairfield and Patti
Provo.
        p.   cm.
    Includes bibliographical references.
    1. Tarot. 2. Self-perception—Miscellanea. I. Provo,
Patti.
II. Title.
BF1879.T2F354   1991
133.3'2424—dc20   91-6563
                                          CIP
ISBN 0-87728-731-7
BJ

Typeset in 12 pt. Caslon
Printed in the United States of America

Contents

Contents—*continued*

List of Illustrations

Acknowledgments

Gail Fairfield would like to say thank you to Debra Clark & Sara Clark for their love and support during the writing of this book.

And I would like to express my gratitude to Pat Kelley for playing the part of the *Fool* in this project. It is she, by way of her endless creative talents, who sparked my own creative fire, setting it ablaze to become the book it is today.

It is Kathi Ray who gave heart to the endless task of creating the *Inspiration Tarot* deck. For me she is the *Sun*. I appreciate and admire the creative "brilliance" that shines through each piece of art she labors over. I acknowledge the energy behind her work in this endeavor, and I am thankful for her patience and faith in me.

Blessings and love go out to Maureen Woodcock. During the book's entire early development—just as in my own—Maureen acted as my *Empress*, my nurturer, my friend. Her contributions are too numerous to mention. Let it suffice to say that if it were not for her and her husband, Bill Woodcock, the dream would have died long ago. She is the *Great Mother* personified. . . . A woman who finds herself in more book dedications than anyone I know.

Thanks also go out to Von Provo (the other part of my own *Lovers* aspect) for setting such a firm foundation from which to build my dreams. And to my children, Jenny, Forest, Kahill, and Nicholas, for learning independence—initially at least—against their wills.

And then there is Rachel Kimmel, someone who has stood by me from the beginning, and, God willing, someone who will be by my side at the end. In her lives the *High Priestess*, ever reminding me that no journey is too difficult if we consciously seek to walk in the light. By her shining example I am humbled.

I would also like to thank Marilyn Foulkes of Peacock Productions for her graphic support, Marge Priest (and partners) for letting me use the cabin space at Reddings Beach to write, and finally, to Leonard Duboff, for being my professional advisor and friend.

—Patti Provo
Vashon Island, WA, 1991

Introduction

*T*he *Inspiration Tarot Workbook* and the *Inspiration Tarot* deck have been designed to encourage you to develop a diary of your personal growth through the process of drawing your own tarot deck.

The concept behind making your own deck has two interwoven purposes. The first and most obvious reason is to establish some familiarity with the composition of a tarot deck. Regardless of the various symbols used within the structure of a deck, all tarot decks contain 78 cards. And they are always divided into two parts. The first part consists of 22 cards and is referred to as the Major Arcana. The second part has 56 Minor Arcana cards grouped into four sets of 14—much like the playing cards decks used for a game of poker today. Even as you casually flip through the pages of the *Workbook*, you will begin to notice these and other patterns in a tarot deck, such as the qualities of the Major Arcana and the nature of the four suits and the number values of the Minor Arcana.

Because each card represents a different aspect of collective human experience, choosing to develop your own symbology for each of those aspects (cards), will mean you have also chosen to become actively involved in a study of your Self.

We wish to further the growing concept and practice of pursuing personal life management through enlightenment—enlightenment taken to mean a transformation from the "darkness" of our limited sensory awareness to a broader perception of reality—one viewed with better "lighting!"

The *Workbook* will lend structure and definition to your creativity by furnishing a format to document the discovery and expression of yourself. We include, as part of that structure, the classic 78-card tarot deck using the traditional titles for the cards. We know that you may choose different forms and titles.

It is assumed that you will want to peruse other tarot decks and books in addition to the *Workbook* to get ideas about how to proceed, but you may also decide to jump in cold and begin your designs right away. Because it is your own deck, you'll go through a process that is just right for you, arriving at a product that is expressive *of* you.

Vicki Noble, Mary Greer, and Gail Fairfield have generously agreed to contribute their efforts to this work. Summarized versions of their card interpretations have been included in the *Workbook*. Vicki Noble is the author of *Motherpeace: A Way to the Goddess through Myth, Art and Tarot* (HarperCollins, 1983), and joint creator with Karen Vogel of the Motherpeace Deck. Among Mary Greer's many credits is *Tarot For Your Self* (Newcastle Publishing, 1984). Gail Fairfield wrote *Choice Centered Tarot*, (first published in 1981, reprinted by Ramp Creek Publishing, 1989). All are highly regarded for their respective expression of the belief that the tarot is an excellent tool for personal transformation. This perspective, of course, is philosophically compatible to our own.

One of the common themes you will notice throughout the *Workbook* then, from all the contributing authors, is the belief that Tarot offers a creative pathway for a journey back to the state of *Self-understanding*. The benefits of personal enlightenment do not end at effective choice making and problem solving on an individual basis, however. We believe that the natural outcome of personal transformation is social transformation. We feel that by viewing reality from a positive perspective and by developing confidence in our ability to create what we want from life, we can direct creative power toward an improved world vision and Earth healing.

In the introduction of her book *Motherpeace*, Vicki Noble talks about her own process of spiritual transformation and the subsequent social contribution she has made using art and tarot. She describes her first drawings of women and children as "light and playful pictures of how I imagined the ancient cultures must have been…," and tells us of her experience drawing the first two tarot cards to replace the two cards missing from the deck her daughters were using. "I decided to draw the missing cards for them, just for fun, without any pressure about perfection. In the simplest way it pleased me."[1]

It is our hope that you experience this same kind of simple delight as you proceed with your personal journey through the pages of *The Inspiration Tarot Workbook*. Since this is a workbook, it essentially becomes a book that you write for yourself. We suggest that at first you read the *Workbook* from cover to cover. Then begin to follow the ideas for familiarizing yourself with tarot as outlined in the book. Draw, doodle, paint, paste-up pictures and write your notes in journal section of the workbook. As you become more comfortable with the tarot as a whole, you'll know when you're ready to launch the second phase of the *Inspiration Tarot* process—drawing the actual deck. Whatever you do, we believe that the more fun you make it, the easier it will be to get to know yourself. In time, your workbook will become a treasured documentation of your personal evolution.

---

[1] Vicki Noble, *Motherpeace: A Way to the Goddess through Myth, Art & Tarot (NY: HarperCollins, 1983), p.12.*

The Purpose of Pictures

Each of the seventy-eight cards in a tarot deck is a symbolic mirror of a corresponding facet of human development. Together they are a pictorial collection of human experience. Like a matrix of universal principles, teachings, and developmental phases, the tarot is an illustrated documentation of the various aspects and processes in human evolution.

The first of two divisions in the deck is the Major Arcana—Arcana meaning *mysteries revealed*. It consists of twenty-two titled cards which characterize the major principles, or life themes, of human experience. Each of the cards has a name, such as the Fool, the Chariot, the Star, and so forth, which uniquely identifies it as a specific aspect of human nature. The remaining fifty-six cards are called the Minor Arcana, and are often referred to as specific challenge or opportunity cards.

To think of each card as a symbolic representation of collective human experience is not enough, however. Whereas the laws of human (spiritual) evolution may never change, the symbology that triggers the "associative recall" that describes those laws often reflects only the values of the society or individual that has developed them.

An example of this is shown when we study, from a historical perspective, any one of the Major Arcana cards drawn during medieval times. When the treasurer of France commissioned Jacquemin Gringonneur to draw three tarot decks for King Charles IV in 1392, the Hierophant, which is the title given today to the card that depicts a religious teacher or person with spiritual authority, was titled "the Pope." In this gilded version of the spiritual leader of the day, the figure is dressed as the Pope. He wore the papal crown and is accompanied by two cardinals. In the Pope's right hand is the key to St. Peter's, and he holds the Gospel on his lap.

Although the principle of this card is that of a philosophical or spiritual leader, using the monarch of the Roman Catholic Church as a symbol is bound to trigger different reactions in different people. In the present day, a picture of the Pope might translate as a symbol of spiritual growth for some and spiritual oppression for others! In order to use the tarot as an effective tool for expanding *your* conscious awareness, it becomes necessary to either discover an established form of symbology that you can relate to, or create specific symbology of your own.

Why Draw Your Own Symbols?

Drawing, card by card, is one way of creating a dialogue between your internal guidance and your external realization. This heightened ability to listen to your Self is an important asset in making conscious choices about the desired direction of your life. Use the workbook as a catalyst; trust yourself.

Consider the awareness that is likely to result from drawing the card designated to represent the principle of cause and effect, *i.e.*, karma. This card is traditionally titled Justice. One method you may choose to use to develop the symbols (or images) for this card, or for any of the cards, is to extract them from your own life experiences. In order to alter your conscious understanding of the principle that Justice depicts, you may begin to observe how your own thoughts and actions (*i.e.*, cause) have an equivalent re-action (*i.e.*, effect) upon the world around you. Watch, or better yet, document, how choosing to spend time (or not spend time) with a son or daughter affects the atmosphere in the family setting. How does the attitude you take to work with you affect co-workers? In light of this expanded awareness, the decisions you make are likely to be different than those you had chosen before your study of the Justice card began. As a result, you can now take a more "active" role in creating your outcomes in the daily events—and the long term goals—of your life. And so it goes with each card.

The Origin of the Tarot

The idea of using the tarot as a tool for self-exploration and growth is not necessarily a new one. We cannot be entirely certain about the origin of the tarot since the most tangible history available begins only as early as the mid-14th century. Other clues as to the original intent of the tarot point to ancient Egypt, where it is thought that it was used to initiate priests into different levels of religious mysteries. Further anthropological studies suggest that the history of the tarot goes back much further where it was created as a lasting testimonial of the way of life during Goddess-worship, and as unwritten mystical teachings intended for our beneficial use, even today. What we do know is that in recorded terms, the traditional application of tarot has often been used by a select number of psychics who acted as advisors to others—primarily rulers or the royal class—especially during the Medieval Period.

People may have believed that psychic ability was a gift "given" to only a chosen few, and that most people did not possess such vision (or intuitive nature) for themselves back then.

Today, however, most people know that intuition is the natural heritage of every human being. More and more people prefer to pursue intuitive judgment for themselves, rather than consulting an oracle.

Some writers speculate that the vast interest in mystical wisdom has re-emerged as a result of a conscious choice to discover ways of *personal* empowerment. The need to regain a feeling of authority in our lives may be motivated by an attempt to override a growing sense of lack of control in a consistently unpredictable environment—either of a personal or social nature. Or, instead of feeling helpless about the outcome of our existence on earth, people are preferring to find ways to feel hopeful. Slogans like, "You have to love peace more than you hate war," are common to many social movements now in existence. We need to possess a feeling of effectiveness in the personal and/or social aspects of our world. And of course, many people possess an innate curiosity about the workings of life, whether they are socially active, personally oppressed, or peacefully content. To them, the "how's and why's" of life provide a lifelong philosophical dedication. Whatever the actual incentive, there is a definite movement in the direction toward accepting individual responsibility in the manifestation of human conditions in the world as a whole.

Which brings us to another purpose of creating the *Inspiration Tarot* deck.

Symbols: A World Language

Whether they are described as pictures, symbols, or even hieroglyphics, written images are keys to communication. All cultures have used symbols to relay ideas and information pertinent to inner cultural values and teachings. However, it is these pictorial symbols that serve best as a bridge between cultural differences. Because they are ubiquitous in nature, they do in fact, create a universal language. As in any pattern of symbols, they are a collective form of communication rather than a personal form. Though essential to conveying thoughts between ourselves and others, it is only when we create a symbol familiar to our own experiences that we begin to communicate with ourselves. Developing a collective language *and* a personal language is one way to better understand ourselves so we can live harmoniously with ourselves and the people around us.

The Inspiration Tarot Workbook gathers some of the symbols most often used on tarot decks. We want you to see some of the ideas that have been used to convey similar messages over the years. Any number of established symbol systems could have been used—from the Chinese I-Ching hexagrams to the twenty-two letters of the Hebrew alphabet. The whole point is that, "Anything goes." Whatever form it takes, from collages or abstracts to word association, the purpose is to develop a triggering device of your own—one that will create the pictures and meanings in your mind that reflect your personal life experience.

CHAPTER

2

The Design Process

One of the best ways to prepare for creating your own tarot deck is to look through other decks in addition to the Inspiration Tarot deck. When studying other decks, notice the variety of styles and symbols that have been used. Group the cards in various ways: Major and Minor Arcana, suits, numbers, colors, or other symbols. Find the patterns within the deck. Spend some time with the cards; notice what you like and dislike about the symbols that others have chosen. Play with the cards for a while—an hour, a day, or a month.

If you don't have access to other decks, you might want to look through *The Encyclopedia of Tarot*[2] for illustration possibilities. You may also choose to read several different tarot authors since each one will describe the concepts uniquely. In keeping with the idea that each tarot card represents a concept that describes a fundamental life experience, it is also important to recognize that each tarotist depicts that concept according to his or her point of view. Chapter 3, which is the journal and sketchbook section of the *Workbook*, will provide you with further descriptions of various interpretations of the cards. Of course, your own intuition is unbeatable when it comes to visual or verbal interpretation. Then, when you feel ready, begin to design your first card.

In working with some cards, you'll get a strong, clear flash of insight and you'll immediately trust it as "true." With other cards, you may want to use modifications of someone else's words and pictures until such time as your own adaptation comes through. What's important is that you have a starting point for understanding each card. From there, direct experiences with the tarot, (such as the idea of watching how the subjective principle of the JUSTICE card works in your own life suggested in chapter 1), will help you expand your possible interpretations.

---

[2] This vast encyclopedia consists of three volumes edited by Stuart Kaplan, published by U.S. Games in 1978, 1985 and 1990.

Creative Settings

Remember your own style for cultivating creativity. Some people like to set aside a regular time for writing, drawing, music or crafts: one hour a day, one day a month, one week per season. Others feel stifled by such a schedule and prefer the "whenever I feel like it" approach. Still others prefer intense drives of activity followed by breaks. You may want to work with music, in silence, with order or with clutter. You may choose to be at home, in the country, in the city, on the water, or in an office. You might prefer to work alone or to collaborate with adults, children, spirit guides, or animals. You may love deadlines or resist them. Your deck may be completed in one week or this may be the beginning of a life-long project. Whatever your criteria, it's important to set up your "taroting" time and space so that it matches your concept of a good place to work or play. Be honest with yourself about your expectations so that, whatever your personal style, your tarot designing can feel successful and ap-

propriate for you. Create a space in your mind and your life for this tarot deck to come into being—your way!

Once you've made room for the tarot, you may instantly know how you want to interpret, symbolize and depict the images for the cards. If that's true for you, jump right into chapters 3 and 4 and start designing. If you are still trying to focus yourself, the following activities can be useful in helping you to tune in your inner voice. Choose whichever of them make sense for you or use them as catalysts for your own methods of generating creativity.

The four steps to designing any tarot card are really easy. You simply choose a card to work on, have an idea about the meaning of the card, choose the picture and/or word symbols that express the meaning of the card for you, and record the symbols on the workbook page with the appropriate blank card.

CHOOSING THE CARD TO DESIGN

If you get stuck in knowing which card to design first, or next, here are some suggestions for choosing a card.

❖ Go from beginning to end: Start from the Fool (0) and go to the World (XXI) in the Major Arcana. Go from Ace through King as you proceed through the Minor Arcana, the Wands, Cups, Swords and Pentacles.

❖ Choose a card intuitively: Pick a card from an already existing deck, take a blank card from the Inspiration Tarot deck, or open this workbook at random and work on the card that is mentioned on that page.

❖ Choose a card by inspiration: Notice which card pops into your mind during the night, during meditation, during a walk, or during a conversation with a friend.

UNDERSTANDING THE CARD

You have intuitive understandings that can be combined with your conscious knowledge to create a personal tarot deck. To follow are some suggestions on how to consciously and unconsciously research the card and come to your own knowing about its meaning. Once you've chosen a particular card as your focus, you will also want to decide whether its traditional name matches your concept of the card. At the beginning of chapter 3 there is an exercise on choosing your own titles if that is something you think you'd like to do. Also, on the workbook pages in the Journal and Sketchbook section, there are several interpretations for each card. When you've decided on a title and an interpretation, you can record your conclusions on the appropriate workbook page. Here are some methods you may want to use to explore the cards and discover the meanings they symbolize for you.

❖ Read the interpretations in this workbook: Think about the similarities and differences among the various interpretations presented here. Look through the explanations on the structure of the *Inspiration Tarot* deck section (page 13) and review the Symbol Glossary in Appendix II

(pages 183-202). Choose the ones you like the best. Find the common theme that goes through all that you've read and seen. Summarize the theme for yourself.

❖ Read other books: Compare the interpretations in this workbook to those in other books. (See Suggested Reading.) Choose phrases you like from the books you have selected, and combine them. Write down your own interpretation. Adapt it as you have more experiences with this card.

❖ Talk about the tarot: Ask your tarot friends what they think the cards mean. Take a class, attend a seminar, go to a professional reader and get some ideas.

❖ Let the card speak to you: In a relaxed state, ask the card what it wants to say and listen for a response. Notice its meaning in a dream. Watch for life events that give you a signal. Position your body in the pose of the card and notice what your body tells you. (There are more details on these kinds of activities in the next section.)

CHOOSING YOUR SYMBOLS

Your interpretational ideas are automatically, unconsciously, symbolized in words and pictures, just as your emotional experiences are symbolized in dreams. Of course, you may not be immediately conscious of tarot symbolism, just as you may not remember your dreams. But, with

practice, the tarot symbols can be coaxed out of your unconscious. Here are some ways to uncover them.

❖ Automatically draw or write: You can use one of the relaxation activities described in this section to allow yourself to tune into a card, or use any other technique that proves effective for you. Then, while holding a drawing or writing tool, allow your unconscious to direct your hand. You can even close your eyes until the drawing is complete. It may take several attempts with this technique before you get past vague squiggles and arrive at symbols that seem "right."

❖ Ask for a dream: Before you take a nap or go to bed at night, note the date and the subject for the dream. You can write something like: Tonight (date) I will dream about symbols for the (name of the card). If you awaken in the night and remember any part of a dream, jot it down. When you wake up in the morning, write or draw whatever you've retained. Even fragments of memory are useful. You may want to do this for several nights; one night may be enough. If you haven't been in the habit of remembering dreams, this technique can help you remember dreams on any topic. Taking Vitamin B6 also seems to aid in dream recall.

❖ Ask for a life event: Take a moment to focus your mind on a particular card and ask that ideas for its symbols come to you during the day (or week). While taking a walk, driving a car, sitting at the beach, working, having lunch with a friend, or going to a movie, you might see, hear, or feel something that symbolizes your card. Carry a note pad or the workbook with you and record images and designs that come to mind.

❖ Move your body: You might want to pose yourself in the traditional position of the card to understand how it feels to embody that card. This works especially well for the Major Arcana. You may enjoy using Yoga, Tai Chi, or some

other ritualized movement as your attuning activity. Or, you may want to move around, freely and unconsciously, and notice the kinds of movements that seem to symbolize your card. Your tarot design could show a person who is demonstrating a particular movement or position. It could also be an abstract or geometric representation of it.

❖ Call on spirit: You can name it God, Goddess, Spirit Guide, Inner Self, Higher Power, the Force, or some personal or cultural name. You can pray to it, call on it, feel its presence, or visualize it. Whatever its name, however you find it, the "something" that is beyond your consciousness is available as a resource for you. Ask it for guidance, ideas, and insight, and notice what comes back to you.

❖ Create a personal ritual: This ritual could include any of the activities above, in whatever sequence makes sense to you. You'll probably want to include an opening or tuning-in process, with one or more activities designed to attune you to your cards, and some kind of closing. (See Suggested Reading for ritual books.)

❖ Create a trance state: Use your favorite relaxation process to enter a light trance state. When you are there, ask yourself to experience the symbols for this particular card. If you have a tape recorder going, you can describe what you see, feel, and hear without coming back to your usual consciousness. Otherwise, as soon as you come back to your normal state, jot down your ideas in words or symbols. If you don't know how to get into a light trance, you could try one of the following ideas:

Listen to Music—something without lyrics. Choose a tape or record that really takes you to a centered, serene place. With your eyes closed, float and drift with the music, repeat the name of the card to yourself and notice what thoughts and images come to your mind.

Listen to a relaxation tape—one that keeps you alert and helps you to tune in to an internal sensitivity. You can use a commercially produced tape or you can create your own (see Appendix I for sample script). Allow the suggestions on the tape to take you into your own personal mind space. Once there, ask to see your tarot card.

Focus on a candle, a crystal—or another ritual object. Allow your attention to become completely centered within the object as you let noises and distractions fade from importance. Once you are in the center of your focusing object, ask the card to appear.

Meditate—in a formal or informal manner. Your style of meditation may involve the use of phrases which you say to yourself or chant out loud. Your meditation might include visualizing a particular image in your mind and concentrating on it. It might mean holding a special physical position which helps you to tune in. Or, you might meditate by holding or touching a specific object—such as a rock, a painting, or a feather—which you can see and feel. Whatever technique you use, once you get into your meditative state, you can utilize it to get ideas about your card.

Ask a friend to guide you—into a light trance state (see sample in Appendix I). Once you're relaxed, have your friend suggest that you see, hear, or feel the card and come to understand its principles. You can then tell your friend what you've experienced and he or she can record it before you come out of the trance.

CREATING THE CARD

Once your personal symbols are conscious, they can be rendered on cards. If you feel hesitant about your own artistry, you can direct someone else in the execution of your design, or you can enhance your self-confidence with help from an artistic friend, or from a one-day workshop at a local studio or art center. You can read about techniques that range from collage art to line drawings. See Suggested Reading for some good how-to books on beginning-art techniques. One in particular is Madeline McMurray's book, *Illuminations, The Healing Image* (Wingbow Press, 1989). It is an excellent guide (as the cover states) to "finding—and

learning from—the inner artist for psychic growth."

Remember that your creations express your identity as it is at this time. While it may be true you have a gift for creating tarot images that speak to many people, you might also want to create a tarot image for yourself. Whether or not your cards are professional in quality, they reflect the truth of you. Later, you might want to change your design. Later you might recognize their perfection! For now, it's your opinion and vision that matters. You have taken the time to become familiar with these cards; you can trust your knowing and ability.

You may want to try several different drawing/art materials in order to find the one that can best express your symbols. Each of the following tools has its own merits and drawbacks. Some smear, and will need to be sprayed with a fixative. Others are light, soft, dark, or bold in nature. Through experimentation, you can find the medium that suits your talents and your ideas. Remember also, that the actual *Inspiration Tarot* deck is made of heavier paper stock than the workbook pages. It was designed to accommodate most, if not all of your artistic creations. You can use the following tools:

Crayons
Pastels
Chalk
Colored Pencils
Water-based Magic Markers
Permanent Magic Markers
Water Colors
Pen and Ink
Collage Images
Photographs
Photocopies of Real Objects
Construction Paper
Art Gum Eraser
Paint Brushes
Scissors
Glue

Use the sketchbook and the blank card pages provided in the workbook to play around with your drawings and designs. When you feel satisfied, copy your final product onto the actual deck. There are two extra cards included in the deck, in case you want to change the traditional names or change your drawings later.

CHAPTER

3

The Major Arcana

The 22 Major Arcana cards represent philosophical concepts, or processes, that affect us on every level of life. These processes can be applied to help us understand the Self, feelings, ideas, and physical realities. They can be utilized personally, professionally or politically. In specific situations, the energy symbolized by some cards is more appropriate to use than the energies in other cards. For example, the nurturance of the EMPRESS might not be appropriate to use with an overly demanding relative; the limits of the DEVIL might not work with an infant. In every situation, however, we can benefit from at least one of the twenty-two themes.

The Major Arcana have been named after the people and things that symbolized these powerful concepts in medieval times. For today, some authors have chosen to rename the cards with titles that suit our times. You may also wish to rename them yourself. On the other hand, once you realize what the titles represent, you may be comfortable with them.

To get used to symbolizing concepts in words and images, you might want to try working with the themes shown in Table 1 on page 12. They are themes of the Major Arcana cards, divorced from their traditional titles. The themes emerge like this: Each card can be seen to represent an attribute or personality characteristic that could describe you or someone else. If you were using the card to explain someone's attribute, you could say, "The person described by this card is... (*fill in the blank from the list below*)." Each card can also represent a process or a way of behaving that could be discussed as follows: "This person is in the process of... (*fill in the blank*)." In either case, the symbols on each card will epitomize these concepts for you. Before you get caught up in the traditional names, take some time to brainstorm about the Major Arcana themes. You can use some of the activities presented in chapter 2 if you want help in focusing your attention.

Now, if you prefer, you can add your titles to those on the Major Arcana workbook pages and decide on your choices for images and interpretations.

Table 1. Attributes and Processes attached to Major Arcana.

Card Number	Attributes	Processes	My Title
0	Faith	Having or creating trust	_____
I	Discernment	Distinguishing differences and similarities	_____
II	Spirituality	Merging with All That Is	_____
III	Nurture	Caretaking	_____
IV	Power	Taking responsibility	_____
V	Morality	Practicing what is preached	_____
VI	Cooperate	Joining together	_____
VII	Control	Directing the action	_____
VIII	Survive	Responding to instinct	_____
IX	Knowledge	Gaining perspective	_____
X	Release	Letting go	_____
XI	Equilibrium	Creating balance or harmony	_____
XII	Willingness	Waiting for guidance	_____
XIII	Transition	Transforming	_____
XIV	Artistry	Blending and creating	_____
XV	Structure	Setting limits and boundaries	_____
XVI	Catalyze	Changing from the inside out	_____
XVII	Resourcefulness	Receiving abundance	_____
XVIII	Guidance	Knowing the way	_____
XIX	Rebirth	Revitalizing	_____
XX	Maturity	Graduating	_____
XXI	Choice	Opening doors	_____

The Structure and Symbols of the Major Arcana

The composition of the Major Arcana cards in the *Inspiration Tarot* deck follows a simple format using traditional titles and traditional correlations to astrological and Tree of Life references, similar to those you would find on other decks you research. Learning the meaning of the symbols we have used on the deck is just one more exercise you may choose to do, as a way to become familiar with the traditional images other people have used.

We have attempted to keep the structure open as much as possible because, again, in your own research, you will discover that many authors have chosen other symbols that are representative of their expression of the meaning of the card. The journal and sketch book section of the Workbook has been designed to encourage you to record your own thoughts and images as you focus on particular cards.

Figure 1 shows how the symbols on the *Inspiration Tarot* deck have been structured: Further explanations of the meanings behind the symbols that are printed on the cards can be found in the Appendix II (pages 183-202).

THE TOP OF THE CARD will always have the Roman Numeral for the position of the card from 0 to XXI.

BOTH THE UPPER RIGHT AND UPPER LEFT CORNERS are left blank for you to draw in your own symbols, if you so choose.

THE BOTTOM CENTER of the card has the traditional title for the card.

THE LOWER LEFT CORNER carries the astrological or planetary sign.

THE LOWER RIGHT CORNER shows the pattern on the Tree of Life. The Roman Numeral for the card will always correlate to the position (Path) of similar meaning on the Tree of Life diagram. (The Paths on the Tree of Life, also in Appendix II, gives a more detailed explanation of this relationship.)

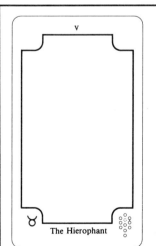

Top of the Card = Roman Numeral

Upper Right Corner = Blank

Upper Left Corner = Blank

Bottom Center of Card = Title

Lower Left Corner = Astrological or Planetary Sign

Lower Right Corner = Pattern on the Tree of Life

Figure 1. The position of the symbols on the Major Arcana cards, in the *Inspiration Tarot* deck.

VI

⚎

The Lovers

NAMES FOR THE CARD

Traditional: ___The Lovers___

Alternatives: ___Ecstasy (Medicine Woman Deck)___

My Choice: ___*Union*___

SYMBOLS

Tree of Life Path: ___*17th Zain*___

Astrological Sign: ___*Gemini*___

Astrological Planet: _____

Colors: _____

Mine: ___*yellow, gold*___

INTERPRETATIONS

Fairfield: You are involved in the process of cooperation. Two or more forces, in coalition will probably never become one unit, they may not work together in all ways, but they do combine energies for a general or specific purpose.

Noble: On the social level, the Lovers symbolizes marriage. In its deeper, esoteric from, the image refers to . . . the coming together of opposite qualities within a being, which leads to wholeness.

Greer: What significant relationship are you involved in? How does this relationship mirror your own sense of self-worth? What needs to be combined, synthesized or brought together?

Mine: ___*The unity between male and female aspects of myself. The balance of two forces.*___

Figure 2. Sample page from the journal and sketchbook section.

How to Fill in the Blank Card Pages

The format for the workbook space for the Major Arcana section includes a reproduction of a card from the *Inspiration Tarot* deck and brief information pertaining to that card. There is writing and drawing space for your own inspirations. (See figure 2).

There are two pages of workbook space for each of the Major Arcana. In the upper left corner of the left-hand page is a reproduction of the actual card with its traditional title. Just to the right of the card is an area which reads NAMES FOR THE CARD. It lists the traditional title and some alternative titles that other authors have used in their own interpretations. The words MY CHOICE are printed on the last line and can be used to note your choice of title for the card on that page.

There is also a list for the names of the symbols that appear on the *Inspiration Tarot* deck. The blank space to the right of each line is for you, should you choose to use this as an exercise for becoming more familiar with the symbols that are pre-printed on the card. Check the Symbol Glossary (Appendix II) to recall the symbols' meanings. The last line on the list is for your symbols. Again, this may be word association for a symbol that you have come up with through research on that card (such as a correlating Hebrew letter) or it can be a freestyle symbol that appeared to you in your sleep one night. This is *your* workbook and any symbol you develop is as valid as any other in its meaning for you. You are not restricted to place the symbol on the outside of the border as has been done with the printed symbols.

On the bottom half of the page there are three brief interpretations of the card. We have specifically chosen authors with various points of view to show you that although the theme for a Major Arcana card may be universal, the interpretation of it is as individual as the person who expressed it.

The final section of the left-hand page has been reserved for your own interpretation. This is where you begin to write down your ideas for the meaning of the card based on a culmination of resources and techniques you have used, either those suggested in chapter 3 of the *Workbook* or any others you have developed.

The right-hand page has an oversize card for your drawings and words. Here, your impressions will become more refined as they are developed from their beginning—perhaps vague conceptual and rough sketch form—to the final images and understandings you will want to carry over first, to the space inside the card that's printed on the left-hand page, and then finally, to the actual deck itself.

The Fool

NAMES FOR THE CARD

Traditional: _____The Fool_____

Alternatives: ___Fool/Child (Voyager Deck), Innocents___

_(Amazon Deck), Seed (Medicine Woman Deck)___

My Choice: _____

_____

SYMBOLS

Tree of Life Path: _____

Astrological Sign: _____

Astrological Planet: _____

Colors: _____

Mine: _____

_____

_____

INTERPRETATIONS

Fairfield: You are experiencing absolute faith and trust in the Universe. You have a feeling of protection and a sense that everything will work out.

Noble: It is the Fool who urges the personality away from lethargy, toward enlightenment, and transformation without fear of the future.... The Fool is about pure spontaneity.... the part of you who just doesn't care what other people think or how things look.

Greer: In what area of your life are you operating entirely on faith and trust? What would be fun to do if you could do anything you wanted?

Mine: _____

_____

_____

_____

THE FOOL

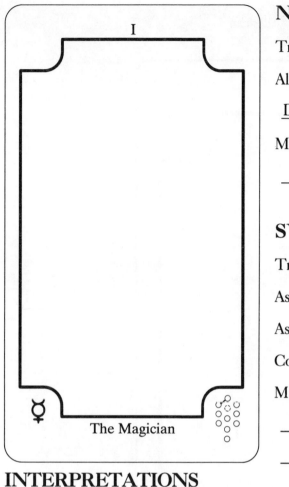

I

The Magician

NAMES FOR THE CARD

Traditional: ___The Magician___

Alternatives: ___Magus (Thoth Deck), Witch (Amazon___

___Deck), Resources (Medicine Woman Deck)___

My Choice: _____

_____

SYMBOLS

Tree of Life Path: _____

Astrological Sign: _____

Astrological Planet: _____

Colors: _____

Mine: _____

_____

_____

INTERPRETATIONS

Fairfield: The Magician appears when you are aware that several different perceptions of reality exist. You might be discriminating between reality and fantasy, among two or more fantasies, or among two or more realities.

Noble: . . . the gift of energy; you are motivated to do, to act, to go forth. With the Magician on your side, you should be able to accomplish whatever you set out to do . . . . Master of the Fire . . . . You may reach out and touch someone else, awakening their life force energies with the intensity of your own.

Greer: Are your objectives clear? What skills and abilities are needed in this situation? What do you want others to believe or see?

Mine: _____

_____

_____

THE MAGICIAN

II

The High Priestess

NAMES FOR THE CARD

Traditional: __The High Priestess__

Alternatives: __Seeker (Medicine Woman Deck), The Seer__

__(Thea's Tarot Deck), Corn Maiden (Native American)__

My Choice: _____

_____

SYMBOLS

Tree of Life Path: _____

Astrological Sign: _____

Astrological Planet: _____

Colors: _____

Mine: _____

_____

_____

INTERPRETATIONS

Fairfield: The High Priestess represents awareness of the greater self. You are in tune with that boundless self, the spiritual part of the self. You have a need to ignore the distractions and limitations of the physical world . . . to tune in to that expanded self.

Noble: . . . your intuition is functioning more strongly than your intellect. A wisdom is activated in you that is older and deeper than your ordinary mode of thinking. . . . The High Priestess invites you to relax and listen to your intuition . . . . to know your feminine self better.

Greer: What do you need to remember or "discover"? How can you best use your intuitive, psychic or dream abilities at this time?

Mine: _____

_____

_____

THE HIGH PRIESTESS

III

♀

The Empress

NAMES FOR THE CARD

Traditional: __The Empress__

Alternatives: __Bounty (Medicine Woman Deck), Matriarch__

__(Amazon Deck), Medicine Woman (Native American)__

My Choice: _____

_____

SYMBOLS

Tree of Life Path: _____

Astrological Sign: _____

Astrological Planet: _____

Colors: _____

Mine: _____

_____

_____

INTERPRETATIONS

Fairfield: You are sensitive to the physical and emotional needs of yourself and others and you are in a position to meet those needs and heal wounds. You are highly dedicated to the nurturing, caretaking process.

Noble: The Empress represents the Great Mother . . . . She promises abundance, birth, growth, harmony, community, and relationship . . . . The Empress is the part of you who engages a partner or mothers a child— she is fundamentally "in relation" to others . . . . a nurturing time for you, a time to nourish yourself as well as others.

Greer: How are your nurturing and mothering qualities being used right now? What creative projects are growing and developing?

Mine: _____

_____

_____

THE EMPRESS

IV

ʘ

The Emperor

NAMES FOR THE CARD

Traditional: ___The Emperor___

Alternatives: ___Command (Medicine Woman Deck),___

___Council Chief (Native American Deck)___

My Choice: _____

_____

SYMBOLS

Tree of Life Path: _____

Astrological Sign: _____

Astrological Planet: _____

Colors: _____

Mine: _____

_____

_____

INTERPRETATIONS

Fairfield: You have committed yourself to identifying with a force that has a great deal of power in the world. In fact, you have chosen to give up one of your individuality or differentness in order to identify with this power.

Noble: ... traditionally a symbol of Patriarchy in its active form .... Sometimes a glyph of fatherhood, he is always an authority figure seeking to establish control and dominance .... Probably the card implies some confrontation with authority, maybe your boss or your father.

Greer: Who is establishing guidelines, parameters and structures in your life? Who has the power and authority, and how is it being used?

Mine: _____

_____

_____

THE EMPEROR

V

The Hierophant

NAMES FOR THE CARD

Traditional: ___The Hierophant___

Alternatives: ___Peacemaker (Medicine Woman Deck),___

___Priestess (Amazon Deck), Shaman (Native American)___

My Choice: _____

_____

SYMBOLS

Tree of Life Path: _____

Astrological Sign: _____

Astrological Planet: _____

Colors: _____

Mine: _____

_____

_____

INTERPRETATIONS

Fairfield: You have chosen to align yourself with a particular philosophy and you feel a great deal of loyalty to it. You are conscientious about living out the philosophy in your daily life and aware of measuring and choosing your actions and behavior based on it.

Noble: . . . the Hierophant may be a minister or other religious leader, or even a psychiatrist—any officer of an orthodoxy who transmits its prevailing beliefs and attempts to adjust people to them . . . . in a reading, it means you are dealing with conventional morality and patriarchal law in some way.

Greer: Who are you looking to for assistance, direction or learning? What traditions are you upholding? What traditions are you rebelling against?

Mine: _____

_____

_____

THE HIEROPHANT

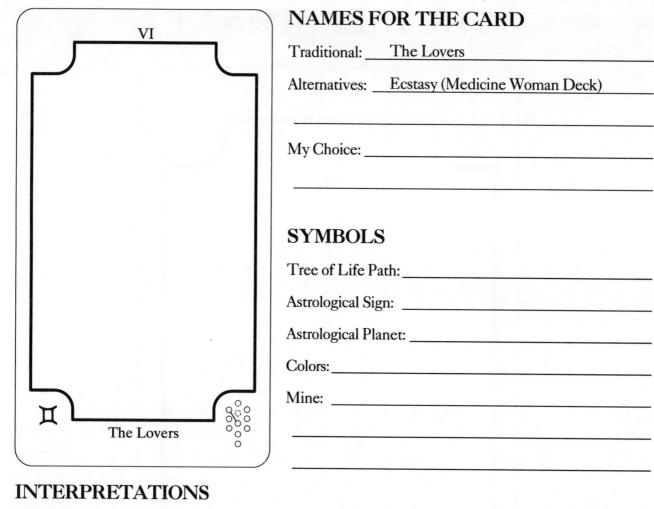

VI

The Lovers

NAMES FOR THE CARD

Traditional: ___The Lovers___

Alternatives: ___Ecstasy (Medicine Woman Deck)___

_____

My Choice: _____

SYMBOLS

Tree of Life Path: _____

Astrological Sign: _____

Astrological Planet: _____

Colors: _____

Mine: _____

_____

INTERPRETATIONS

Fairfield: You are involved in the process of cooperation. Two or more forces, in coalition will probably never become one unit, they may not work together in all ways, but they do combine energies for a general or specific purpose.

Noble: On the social level, the Lovers symbolizes marriage. In its deeper, esoteric form, the image refers to . . . the coming together of opposite qualities within a being, which leads to wholeness.

Greer: What significant relationship are you involved in? How does this relationship mirror your own sense of self-worth? What needs to be combined, synthesized or brought together?

Mine: _____

_____

_____

_____

THE LOVERS

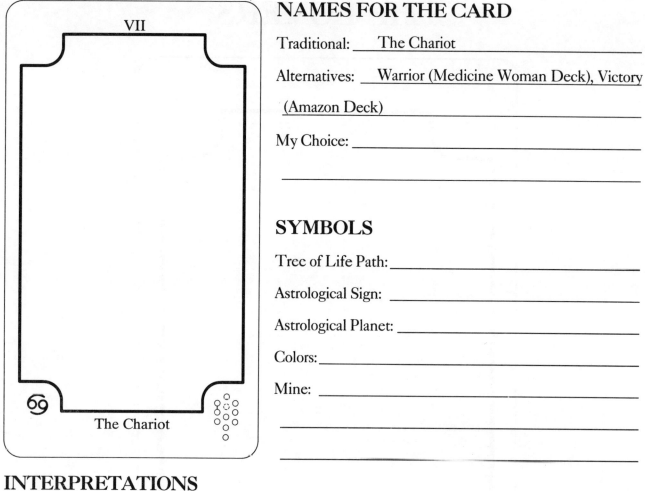

VII

The Chariot

NAMES FOR THE CARD

Traditional: ____The Chariot____

Alternatives: ____Warrior (Medicine Woman Deck), Victory____

(Amazon Deck) ____

My Choice: _____

_____

SYMBOLS

Tree of Life Path: _____

Astrological Sign: _____

Astrological Planet: _____

Colors: _____

Mine: _____

_____

_____

INTERPRETATIONS

Fairfield: You are totally in tune with a fast-moving process or event. By immersing yourself in it, you have become part of it and are therefore able to direct its course.

Noble: ... groundedness and the ability to accomplish tasks on a physical plane. It also traditionally symbolizes a victory of self-discipline .... a time in which you are keeping a strong division between your work life and your feelings, but you have the ability to bridge the gap and connect the two.

Greer: What contradictions and tensions are you struggling to maintain control over? What progress are you making in testing your abilities in the world?

Mine: _____

_____

_____

_____

THE CHARIOT

VIII

Strength

NAMES FOR THE CARD

Traditional: ___Strength___

Alternatives: ___Lust (Thoth Deck), Healing (Medicine___

___Woman Deck)___

My Choice: _____

_____

SYMBOLS

Tree of Life Path: _____

Astrological Sign: _____

Astrological Planet: _____

Colors: _____

Mine: _____

_____

_____

INTERPRETATIONS

Fairfield: You are responding to a force that is not logical, and not even intuitive: it is just a compelling drive. It seems like a biological, emotional, or spiritual survival mechanism that has been triggered without your conscious awareness.

Noble: . . . the power of healing by the laying on of the feminine force. . . . you are experiencing yourself as ready and able to get what you want in life . . . . Your moral Strength is alive right now, your courage and sense of conviction powerful as you express your feelings openly and move others in this way.

Greer: How are you being called upon to show courage and perseverance? What inner passions need to be expressed and reconciled?

Mine: _____

_____

_____

STRENGTH

IX

The Hermit

NAMES FOR THE CARD

Traditional: _____The Hermit_____

Alternatives: ___Crone (Motherpeace Deck), Guide___

___(Medicine Woman Deck), Sage (Amazon Deck)___

My Choice: _____

_____

SYMBOLS

Tree of Life Path: _____

Astrological Sign: _____

Astrological Planet: _____

Colors: _____

Mine: _____

_____

_____

INTERPRETATIONS

Fairfield: You are temporarily withdrawing from others or from your normal environment in order to get some perspective on your situation. You feel that you have gathered enough data and information and you have enough personal wisdom to sort things out on your own.

Noble: Initiate, seeker, and hermit, the Crone represents a stage of life in which wisdom is sought—a time of introversion and spiritual seeking. . . . You are at a crossroads, a time of decision and renewal . . . . time to learn about the magic and powers of divination and prophesy, maybe to use the Tarot, or *I Ching*, maybe to keep a dream journal.

Greer: What are you doing with the time you have to yourself? What concerns about time do you have?

Mine: _____

_____

_____

THE HERMIT

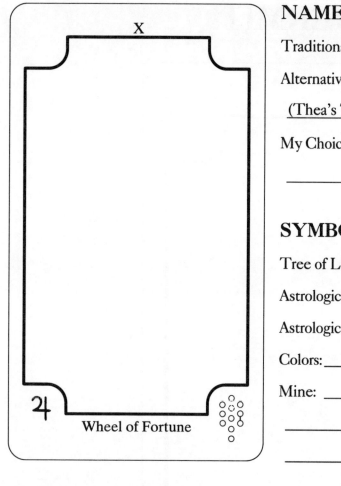

X

♃

Wheel of Fortune

NAMES FOR THE CARD

Traditional: ___Wheel of Fortune___

Alternatives: ___Harvest (Medicine Woman Deck), Comet___

___(Thea's Tarot Deck)___

My Choice: _____

_____

SYMBOLS

Tree of Life Path: _____

Astrological Sign: _____

Astrological Planet: _____

Colors: _____

Mine: _____

_____

_____

INTERPRETATIONS

Fairfield: Something has been triggered or started that will roll to its appropriate resting place. You have done everything that can be done to get things moving. You are waiting to see how others, or the Universal energies, respond.

Noble: . . . Fortune is smiling on you . . . . when something has been wished for and worked toward, it is the Goddess Fortuna who decides on the timing of the event. The Wheel of Fortune signifies a high point, a wish coming true, the manifestation of something anticipated.

Greer: What effects are you feeling from circumstances you put in motion previously? Is there something you need to resolve?

Mine: _____

_____

_____

WHEEL OF FORTUNE

XI

Justice

NAMES FOR THE CARD

Traditional: ___Justice___

Alternatives: ___Adjustment (Thoth Deck) In some___

___decks, this card may be numerically interchanged with___

___the VIII card (Strength).___

My Choice: _____

SYMBOLS

Tree of Life Path: _____

Astrological Sign: _____

Astrological Planet: _____

Colors: _____

Mine: _____

_____

_____

INTERPRETATIONS

Fairfield: You are establishing equilibrium or balance in your life. Like a pendulum that has been pulled too far to one side, you are naturally swinging in the opposite direction. The present situation, whatever it is, will pass and be balanced out by its opposite.

Noble: . . . you are coming to consciousness about your place in the universal scheme of things . . . . You are moving to accept your reality and responsibility for your past choices . . . . You are flowing with the natural cycles of life, following natural laws.

Greer: What is the appropriate compensation (or "energy exchange") needed to balance the situation? What do you need to do to be true to yourself?

Mine: _____

_____

_____

JUSTICE

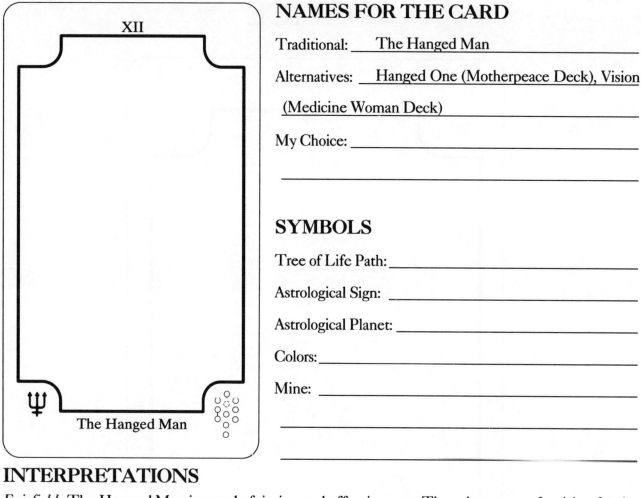

XII

The Hanged Man

NAMES FOR THE CARD

Traditional: ___The Hanged Man___

Alternatives: ___Hanged One (Motherpeace Deck), Vision___

___(Medicine Woman Deck)___

My Choice: _____

_____

SYMBOLS

Tree of Life Path: _____

Astrological Sign: _____

Astrological Planet: _____

Colors: _____

Mine: _____

_____

INTERPRETATIONS

Fairfield: The Hanged Man is a card of timing and effectiveness. There is a sense of waiting for the appropriate time, situation, or circumstances. You are hanging around, suspended in mid-air, waiting to make the next move.

Noble: . . . fundamentally represents the voluntary surrender to a death and resurrection process celebrated in shamanism . . . . in a reading, what it means is not that you are going to die, but that you are going to lose yourself . . . . the Hanged One does not imply crucifixion or pain, but rather a sense of ecstasy and surrender to love.

Greer: What do you expect from the sacrifices you are making? What do you need to get straight? How are you seeking higher knowledge?

Mine: _____

_____

_____

THE HANGED MAN

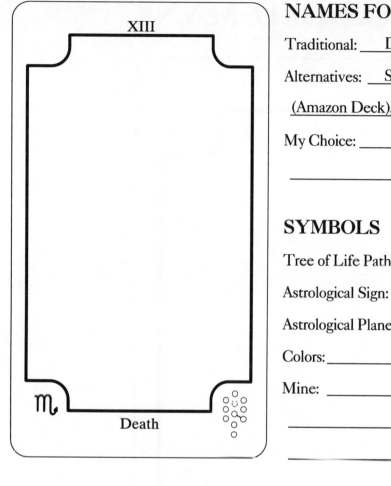

NAMES FOR THE CARD

Traditional: Death

Alternatives: Sunset (Medicine Woman Deck), Crone

(Amazon Deck), The Juggler (Thea's Tarot Deck)

My Choice: _____

_____

SYMBOLS

Tree of Life Path: _____

Astrological Sign: _____

Astrological Planet: _____

Colors: _____

Mine: _____

_____

_____

INTERPRETATIONS

Fairfield: You are experiencing a total change, transformation, or metamorphosis. You need to destroy the old in order to generate something new out of its ashes.

Noble: Death is change . . . . it almost never signifies physical death, but acts as a metaphor for some experience of dying and rebirth in your life . . . . the change is essential and final, and the rebirth is already taking place.

Greer: What do you need to let go of? What is being transformed? What new growth is now possible?

Mine: _____

_____

_____

_____

DEATH

XIV

Temperance

NAMES FOR THE CARD

Traditional: ___Temperance___

Alternatives: ___Art (Thoth/Voyager Deck), Blend (Medicine Woman Deck), Weaver (Native American Deck)___

My Choice: _____

_____

SYMBOLS

Tree of Life Path: _____

Astrological Sign: _____

Astrological Planet: _____

Colors: _____

Mine: _____

_____

_____

INTERPRETATIONS

Fairfield: You are blending diverse elements to create something new. You combine the many elements, allowing them to affect and transform each other. Together they mesh and blend into a new whole.

Noble: . . . the process of blending the parts of the self until fusion is achieved . . . . an integration of the emotional forces with the physical—a blessed union of opposites within and without . . . . The natural movements of energy around and within you are in harmony and integrated.

Greer: What are you feeling optimistic about? How are you combining the resources available to you? What needs to be healed or brought into balance?

Mine: _____

_____

_____

TEMPERANCE

XV

₿

The Devil

NAMES FOR THE CARD

Traditional: ___The Devil___

Alternatives: ___Devil's Play (Voyager Deck), Trickster___

___(Medicine Woman Deck), Oppression (Thea's Tarot Deck)___

My Choice: _____

_____

SYMBOLS

Tree of Life Path: _____

Astrological Sign: _____

Astrological Planet: _____

Colors: _____

Mine: _____

_____

_____

INTERPRETATIONS

Fairfield: You are experiencing some boundaries and limits in your life . . . . your options and choices are being narrowed and your life is becoming more structured.

Noble: You are in some way subscribing to the dominance-submission mentality, and the issue of power is at stake . . . . Whether you are the person wielding the power or the one feeling the effects of submission to authority, your soul is in need of liberation.

Greer: What are the current boundaries and limitations in your life? How can you channel and structure your energies and desires in creative and nonmanipulative ways?

Mine: _____

_____

_____

_____

THE DEVIL

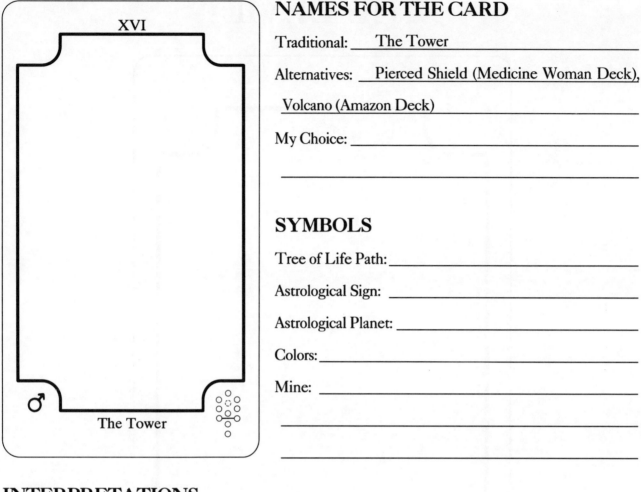

XVI

♂

The Tower

NAMES FOR THE CARD

Traditional: ___The Tower___

Alternatives: ___Pierced Shield (Medicine Woman Deck),___

___Volcano (Amazon Deck)___

My Choice: _____

_____

SYMBOLS

Tree of Life Path: _____

Astrological Sign: _____

Astrological Planet: _____

Colors: _____

Mine: _____

_____

_____

INTERPRETATIONS

Fairfield: You have changed a basic core belief in your life. You are seeing a new "truth" about the way things are for you. That flash of enlightenment is like the lightning bolt hitting the tower. It starts off a whole chain reaction.

Noble: . . . an earthshaking stroke of illumination and the end of false consciousness . . . . in a reading, brace yourself—you're in for a change. A radical shift is taking place . . . a flash of illumination. Whether or not you like what you see, you see it.

Greer: What are you angry about? What structures in your life are breaking up? What has shattered your complacency?

Mine: _____

_____

_____

THE TOWER

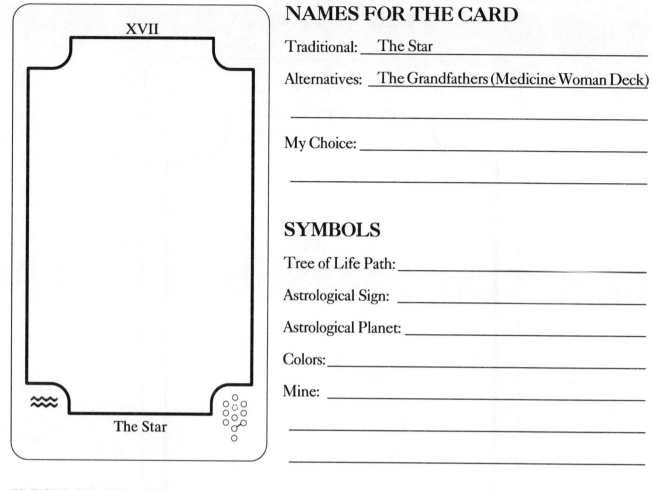

XVII

The Star

NAMES FOR THE CARD

Traditional: __The Star__

Alternatives: __The Grandfathers (Medicine Woman Deck)__

_____

My Choice: _____

_____

SYMBOLS

Tree of Life Path: _____

Astrological Sign: _____

Astrological Planet: _____

Colors: _____

Mine: _____

_____

_____

INTERPRETATIONS

Fairfield: You are experiencing the boundless, free abundance of the Universe. A flow of pure energy is available to you, in the form of resources that can be used for many purposes.

Noble: ... the calm after the storm. The raging fires of the Tower have subsided, a light rain falls, and grace descends like the mist itself.... in a reading you know you have passed to a new level and something in you has opened to the Goddess.... You can feel beauty radiating through your very being, from the center out.

Greer: What aspect of your life is being purified or cleansed? What is being renewed? What are you inspired to do?

Mine: _____

_____

_____

THE STAR

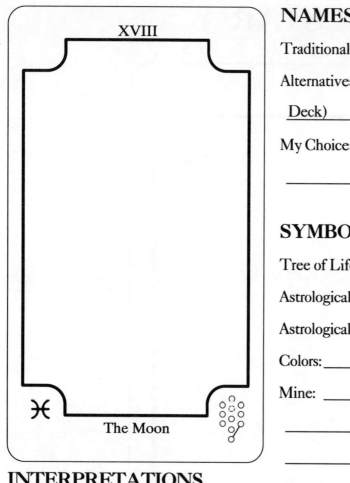

XVIII

The Moon

NAMES FOR THE CARD

Traditional: ___The Moon___

Alternatives: ___The Grandmothers (Medicine Woman___

___Deck)_____

My Choice: _____

_____

SYMBOLS

Tree of Life Path: _____

Astrological Sign: _____

Astrological Planet: _____

Colors: _____

Mine: _____

_____

_____

INTERPRETATIONS

Fairfield: You are being guided by your greater, or Universal, self. You realize that you're getting symbolic messages, showing you the path you need to follow. You're trusting something other than your logical mind to be your guide.

Noble: The Moon represents the core of the ancient female mysteries—the journey into the laby–rinth . . . . a sign of unconsciousness . . . . if you can trust in the higher powers to guide you intuitively through the journey of the darkness and the unknown, then you will learn from the voyage and gain consciousness as your initiatory gift.

Greer: What do you instinctively want to do? Are your actions appropriate to this particular situation or are you responding to some past situation?

Mine: _____

_____

_____

THE MOON

XIX

⊙

The Sun

NAMES FOR THE CARD

Traditional: ___The Sun___

Alternatives: ___Rebirth (Medicine Woman Deck)___

_____

My Choice: _____

_____

SYMBOLS

Tree of Life Path: _____

Astrological Sign: _____

Astrological Planet: _____

Colors: _____

Mine: _____

_____

_____

INTERPRETATIONS

Fairfield: You are experiencing a time of rekindled enthusiasm. You have learned a great deal from past experiences and now you're ready to make refinements and adjustments so that you can do something you've done before in a new and more effective manner.

Noble: . . . the knowledge that we are connected by the eternal rays of the life force, each of us part of a vast organism called "humanity" and the even greater body of Earth itself . . . . You are probably experiencing a great deal of expansiveness and pleasure—your Sun is shining . . . a very creative period for you and the people around you.

Greer: What have you birthed or brought forward to fruition? What joys are you sharing with others?

Mine: _____

_____

_____

THE SUN

XX

Judgment

NAMES FOR THE CARD

Traditional: __Judgment__

Alternatives: __The Aeon (Thoth Deck), Time-Space__

__(Voyager Deck), Muse (Amazon Deck)__

My Choice: _____

_____

SYMBOLS

Tree of Life Path: _____

Astrological Sign: _____

Astrological Planet: _____

Colors: _____

Mine: _____

_____

_____

INTERPRETATIONS

Fairfield: You are experiencing the natural process of growth and maturation. You've matured through the passage of time. You may be celebrating your "coming of age" through a rite of passage or ritual.

Noble: . . . [a] "moment of truth" when the heart can look with complete forgiveness on the personality . . . . You are not angry, and are not blaming others, but taking full responsibility for a choice and for a new way of viewing reality. You are making wise judgements.

Greer: What judgment is being made? What new realization or epiphany is transforming you? What or whom are you responsible for?

Mine: _____

_____

_____

JUDGMENT

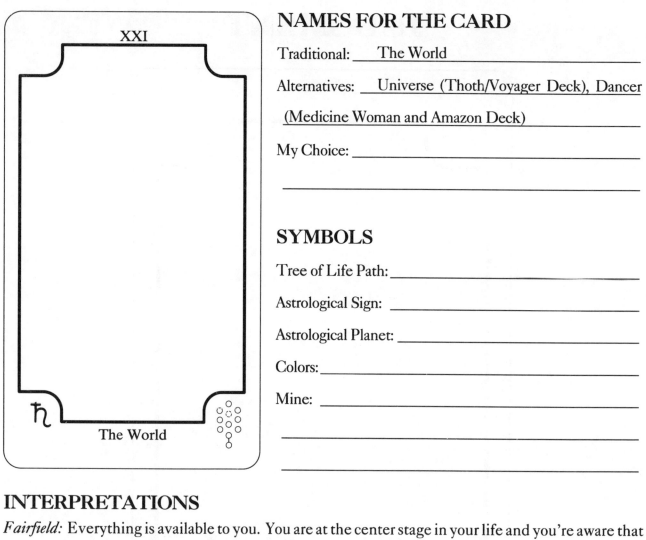

XXI

ħ

The World

NAMES FOR THE CARD

Traditional: ___The World___

Alternatives: ___Universe (Thoth/Voyager Deck), Dancer___

___(Medicine Woman and Amazon Deck)___

My Choice: _____

_____

SYMBOLS

Tree of Life Path: _____

Astrological Sign: _____

Astrological Planet: _____

Colors: _____

Mine: _____

_____

_____

INTERPRETATIONS

Fairfield: Everything is available to you. You are at the center stage in your life and you're aware that you can simply reach out and choose one of many options.

Noble: . . . you have in some sense mastered the three planes of mind, body, and emotions . . . . You are in a state of knowing all your parts—and using them for the expression of your real self in the world.

Greer: What potential do you see in yourself? In the world? What is making you dance for joy?

Mine: _____

_____

_____

_____

_____

THE WORLD

The Minor Arcana

The four suits of the Minor Arcana symbolize the four elements of our world. The elements have various forms of energy to them. Each element's energy has come to represent an influence on specific parts of our lives such as; areas of focus, attention, and activity. In order to understand the suits on the Minor Arcana, therefore, it is valuable to first understand these four dimensions (elements) of life. (See Tarot Suits in Appendix II for further information.)

The suit of Wands represents the element of Fire. It is associated with the spark of essence or soul within each of us that makes us unique. We all have identities and personalities that are representations of that essential force within. The Wands show ways we are naming and expressing ourselves in the world.

The Cups reflect the energy of Water. They deal with emotions and the ways we show or contain our feelings. Since our relationships with others are frequently emotional in nature, the suit of Cups is also about relationships. Additionally, intuition is associated with the suit of Cups because it is the ability to know through feeling (instead of thinking).

The Swords belong to Air. They symbolize the conscious mind. Thinking, communicating, and all the technology associated with the exchange of thoughts and ideas are, clearly, Swords activities. Since the logical mind loves planning and theorizing, time, and time management are Swords concerns, too.

The last suit is that of Pentacles, or Earth. These cards symbolize our connection to the physical world, representing anything we can touch or hold. This includes everything from cars, houses, and money to health, sex and exercise. Additionally, Pentacles cards are reflective of the sensation of groundedness, stability, or safety.

These four suits, and applications of them, cover the areas of life in which activities and experiences occur. The numbers within each suit show the nature of the events that happen. The internal consistency within the tarot dictates that, just as all the Wands have a commonalty, all the cards of one number share a meaning as well. For example, if the Cups cards represent, among other things, emotions, and Fours represent manifesting, then the 4 of Cups

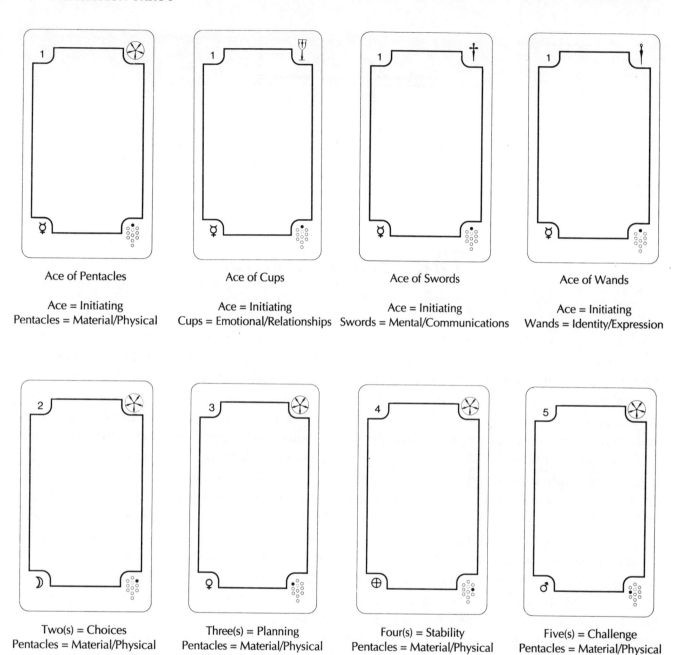

Ace of Pentacles

Ace = Initiating
Pentacles = Material/Physical

Ace of Cups

Ace = Initiating
Cups = Emotional/Relationships

Ace of Swords

Ace = Initiating
Swords = Mental/Communications

Ace of Wands

Ace = Initiating
Wands = Identity/Expression

Two(s) = Choices
Pentacles = Material/Physical

Three(s) = Planning
Pentacles = Material/Physical

Four(s) = Stability
Pentacles = Material/Physical

Five(s) = Challenge
Pentacles = Material/Physical

The area that an experience occurs is depicted with a suit. The nature of an experience is depicted with a number.

Figure 3. An example of the card patterns for suit and number.

could represent "Manifesting Emotions." (See figure 3.)

The basic meanings for the number (PIP) cards from Ace through Ten are as follows:

ACE—beginning, initiating, conceiving, starting

TWO—confirming, affirming, choosing, deciding

THREE—planning, preparing, projecting, detailing

FOUR—doing, manifesting, solidifying, creating

FIVE—adapting, adjusting, changing, challenging

SIX—cycling, repeating, making rhythms, patterning

SEVEN—expanding, varying, experimenting, stimulating

EIGHT—contracting, organizing, structuring, limiting

NINE—flowing, moving, integrating, processing

TEN—hesitating, waiting, taking time out

The last four cards in each suit are called the Court cards. They represent qualities that indicate a greater degree of commitment and/or fulfillment than the Pip cards. They reflect a conscious degree of choice-making with regard to the matters of their suits. Many tarotists feel that the appearance and gender of the Court cards symbolize specific individuals in a person's life. However, it is our feeling that the Court card qualities can be applied to anyone, regardless of gender or appearance. For example, the Queen of Cups represents emotional maturity and competence. These qualities can obviously be ascribed to either sex. (See Court cards and the Tree of Life in Appendix II.) The basic meanings of the Court cards are as follows:

PAGE—risking, daring, committing, jumping in

KNIGHT—focusing, concentrating, fixating, intensifying

QUEEN—maturing, competence, fulfilling, ripening

KING—completing, releasing, sharing, letting go

As you set out to design your Minor Arcana cards, you might want to consider colors, forms, patterns, and symbols that will consistently reflect the energies of the four suits and the processes of numbers.

The Structure and Symbols of the Minor Arcana

The symbols on the *Inspiration* deck for the Minor Arcana follow a consistent structure, similar to that of the Major Arcana with the exception of the use of titles. Brief meanings of all the symbols we have used can be found in Appendix II (pages 183-202).

The "system" we have designed is shown in figure 4 on page 64. The cards are marked as follows:

THE UPPER RIGHT CORNER is the suit of the card.

THE UPPER LEFT CORNER has an arabic numeral on it from 1 to 10, with the exception of the four Court cards which will have the alphabetical initial for the card (i.e., K for King, etc.) This represents the number process of the card. Refer back to the explanation that was given earlier as to specific meanings or assigned "process" that each number possesses.

THE LOWER RIGHT CORNER contains the pattern on the Tree of Life. The number of the card will always correlate with the same number of the Sephiroth (sphere) on the Tree of Life. (See the Tree of Life Graph in Appendix II for an illustrated description of the numbers of the spheres.) For example, all the Tens will have the symbol for the position of the tenth Sephira on the lower right corner. The nines will have the ninth Sephira as its symbol in the lower right corner, and so on.

THE LOWER LEFT is designated for the planetary or astrological symbol.

You can see that a number of styles of symbols were used on the *Inspiration Tarot* deck. This is just one approach in showing you that there are several ways to communicate the same idea. The *Workbook* was designed to help you find your own style—one that communicates to *you*.

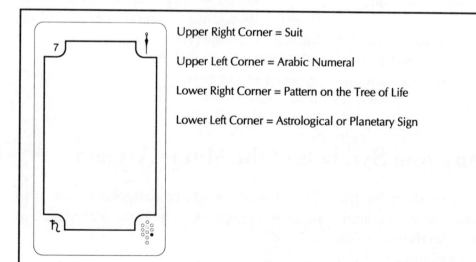

Figure 4. The position of the symbols on the Minor Arcana cards, in the *Inspiration Tarot*

How to Fill in the Blank Card Pages

Even before your entire deck is designed, you will begin to see the patterns of symbols used to illustrate the life forces (or energies) at hand in the daily events of your life. The tarot can be used as a tool to help make constructive choices about your direction—especially if you become keenly aware of the part your will plays in the outcome of that direction.

Like the page format for the Major Arcana, here too, we have reproduced a card the same size as one from the *Inspiration Tarot* deck, along with other authors' interpretations for that specific card. Again we have devoted two pages of workbook space to each card, even though the Minor cards are objective in nature—representing our outer experiences—and are considered to be less complex in their meaning than the Major Arcana cards.

The left-hand page for the Minor Arcana is similar to the left-hand page in Major Arcana section. To the right of the card is an area for the various names of the card (Pages are also depicted as Princesses; Knights as Sons, etc.) with lines at the end of sentence called MY CHOICE so you can add your own ideas.

Below that section is also a list of symbols that appear on the *Inspiration Tarot* deck. Just as is the case with the Major Arcana chapter, the space to the right of each line is for your use. If you like, you can look up the symbols depicted on the card in Appendix II (pages 183-202) and write down the meanings. It is one more way to understand some of the traditional symbols that are used to activate an image of the card while, at the same time, helping you to design your own card. Notice that the last line is for your own significant symbols.

The bottom of the page contains three other interpretations of the card with space at the end for your own version of the card's meaning.

Use the right-hand page in this section just as you would in the Major Arcana section. Draw your symbols and words as the impressions come to you. Then, when you want to, carry them over to the space inside the card that is printed on the left-hand page. When you are ready, you can then draw your final forms onto the actual *Inspiration Tarot* deck.

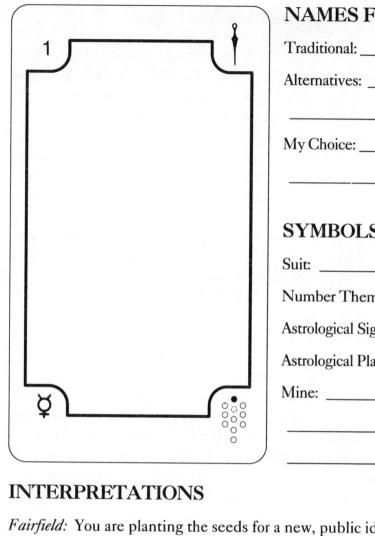

NAMES FOR THE CARD

Traditional: ___Ace of Wands___

Alternatives: ___Rods/Staves/Pipes/Sticks/Scepters___

_____

My Choice: _____

_____

SYMBOLS

Suit: _____

Number Theme: _____

Astrological Sign: _____

Astrological Planet: _____

Mine: _____

_____

_____

INTERPRETATIONS

Fairfield: You are planting the seeds for a new, public identity.

Noble: . . . the beginning of fire—spirit, intuition, energy . . . . A rebirth of spirit.

Greer: How do you want to express yourself creatively? What new opportunity is being offered to you?

Mine: _____

_____

_____

_____

ACE OF WANDS

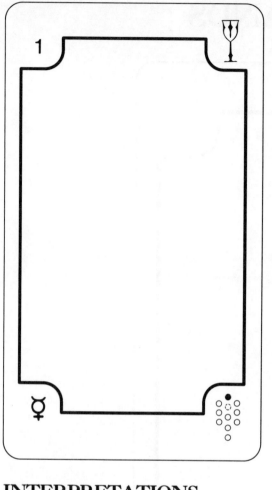

NAMES FOR THE CARD

Traditional: __Ace of Cups__

Alternatives: __Bowls/Chalices/Vessels__

_____

My Choice: _____

_____

SYMBOLS

Suit: _____

Number Theme: _____

Astrological Sign: _____

Astrological Planet: _____

Mine: _____

_____

_____

INTERPRETATIONS

Fairfield: A new emotion. The seed of love, anger, jealousy or another emotion has been planted.

Noble: ... the gift of love—a dive into one's deepest feelings .... a surrender to emotions and beauty.

Greer: What or who is offering you nurturing or love? What does your heart feel most open to?

Mine: _____

_____

_____

_____

_____

ACE OF CUPS

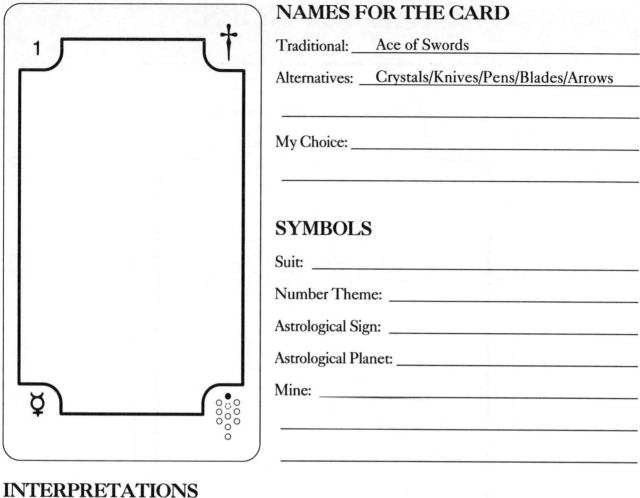

NAMES FOR THE CARD

Traditional: _____Ace of Swords_____

Alternatives: _____Crystals/Knives/Pens/Blades/Arrows_____

_____

My Choice: _____

_____

SYMBOLS

Suit: _____

Number Theme: _____

Astrological Sign: _____

Astrological Planet: _____

Mine: _____

_____

_____

INTERPRETATIONS

Fairfield: A new idea. A brand new lifestyle or direction. The possibility to manifest your philosophy in a new way.

Noble: . . . the gift of intellect, the place where thought begins.

Greer: What new problem are your confronting? What decision do you need to face?

Mine: _____

_____

_____

_____

ACE OF SWORDS

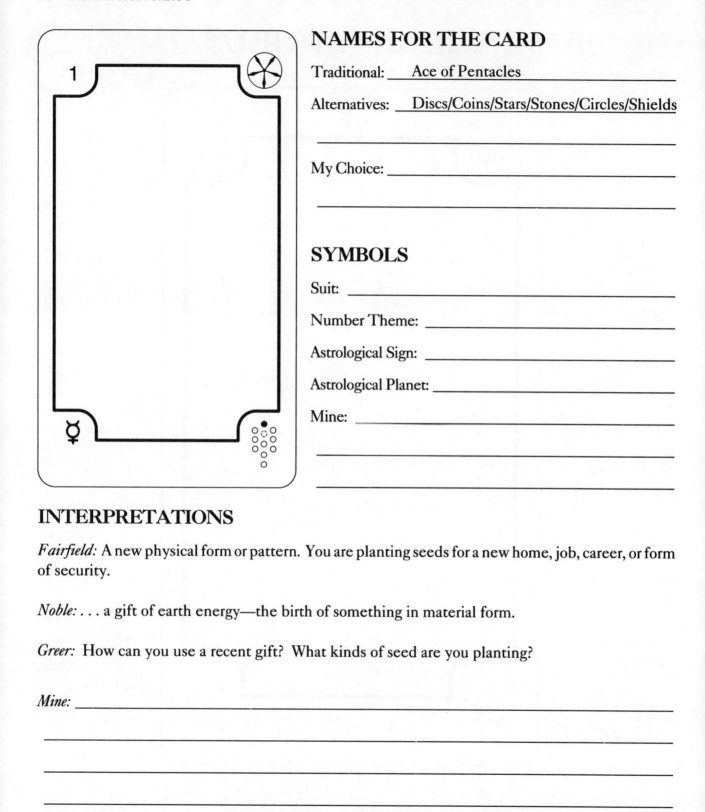

NAMES FOR THE CARD

Traditional: _____Ace of Pentacles_____

Alternatives: ___Discs/Coins/Stars/Stones/Circles/Shields___

_____

My Choice: _____

_____

SYMBOLS

Suit: _____

Number Theme: _____

Astrological Sign: _____

Astrological Planet: _____

Mine: _____

_____

_____

INTERPRETATIONS

Fairfield: A new physical form or pattern. You are planting seeds for a new home, job, career, or form of security.

Noble: . . . a gift of earth energy—the birth of something in material form.

Greer: How can you use a recent gift? What kinds of seed are you planting?

Mine: _____

_____

_____

_____

ACE OF PENTACLES

NAMES FOR THE CARD

Traditional: ___Two of Wands___

Alternatives: ___Rods/Staves/Pipes/Sticks/Scepters___

My Choice: _____

SYMBOLS

Suit: _____

Number Theme: _____

Astrological Sign: _____

Astrological Planet: _____

Mine: _____

INTERPRETATIONS

Fairfield: Claiming and validating the Self. You are saying "yes" to a new role that you've decided to play.

Noble: . . . the harnessing of one's personal power—learning how to use the fire that was born in the Ace.

Greer: What two ideas are you bringing together in a new and different way? What conflicting desires do you wish to integrate?

Mine: _____

TWO OF WANDS

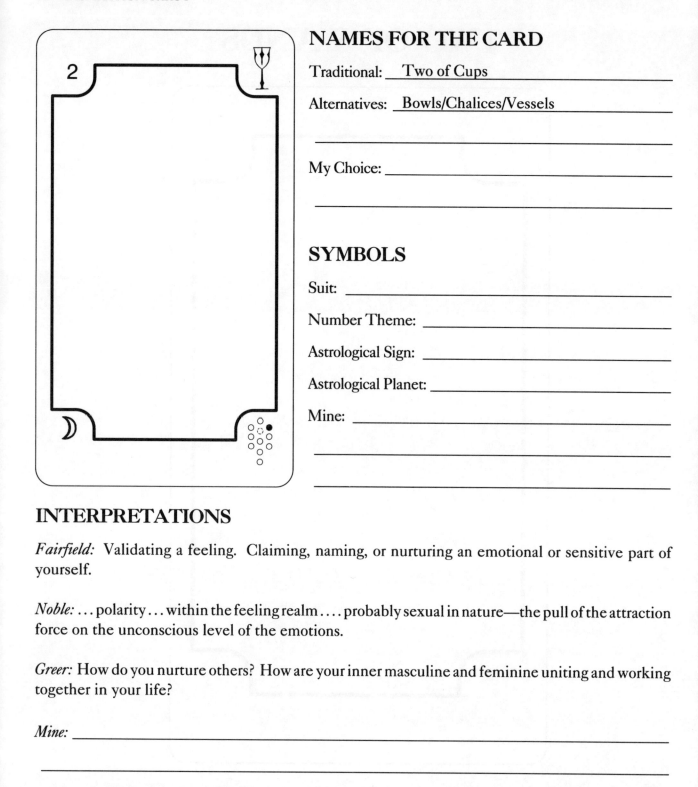

NAMES FOR THE CARD

Traditional: __Two of Cups__

Alternatives: __Bowls/Chalices/Vessels__

_____

My Choice: _____

_____

SYMBOLS

Suit: _____

Number Theme: _____

Astrological Sign: _____

Astrological Planet: _____

Mine: _____

_____

_____

INTERPRETATIONS

Fairfield: Validating a feeling. Claiming, naming, or nurturing an emotional or sensitive part of yourself.

Noble: ... polarity ... within the feeling realm .... probably sexual in nature—the pull of the attraction force on the unconscious level of the emotions.

Greer: How do you nurture others? How are your inner masculine and feminine uniting and working together in your life?

Mine: _____

_____

_____

TWO OF CUPS

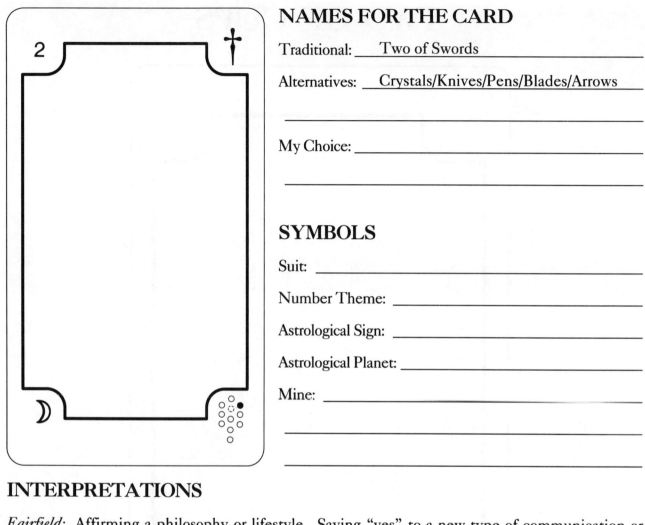

NAMES FOR THE CARD

Traditional: _____Two of Swords_____

Alternatives: ___Crystals/Knives/Pens/Blades/Arrows___

_____

My Choice: _____

_____

SYMBOLS

Suit: _____

Number Theme: _____

Astrological Sign: _____

Astrological Planet: _____

Mine: _____

_____

_____

INTERPRETATIONS

Fairfield: Affirming a philosophy or lifestyle. Saying "yes" to a new type of communication or language. The nurturing of an idea.

Noble: . . . an attempt to gain mental balance and peace. The mind wants to be still, to avoid dealing with whatever might be happening in the external world.

Greer: What are you struggling to maintain in balance?

Mine: _____

_____

_____

_____

TWO OF SWORDS

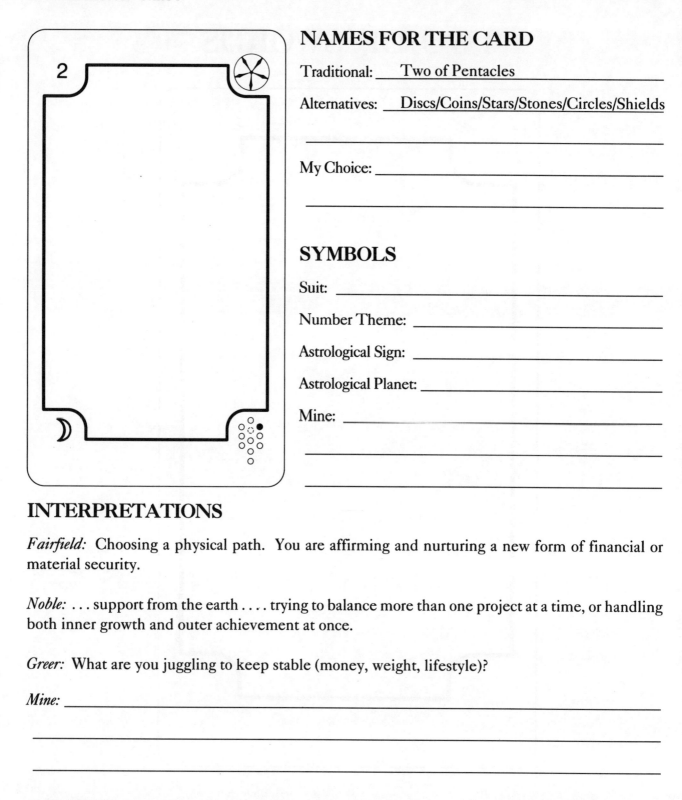

NAMES FOR THE CARD

Traditional: _____Two of Pentacles_____

Alternatives: ___Discs/Coins/Stars/Stones/Circles/Shields___

_____

My Choice: _____

_____

SYMBOLS

Suit: _____

Number Theme: _____

Astrological Sign: _____

Astrological Planet: _____

Mine: _____

_____

_____

INTERPRETATIONS

Fairfield: Choosing a physical path. You are affirming and nurturing a new form of financial or material security.

Noble: ... support from the earth .... trying to balance more than one project at a time, or handling both inner growth and outer achievement at once.

Greer: What are you juggling to keep stable (money, weight, lifestyle)?

Mine: _____

_____

_____

_____

TWO OF PENTACLES

NAMES FOR THE CARD

Traditional: _____ Three of Wands _____

Alternatives: _____ Rods/Staves/Pipes/Sticks/Scepters _____

_____

My Choice: _____

_____

SYMBOLS

Suit: _____

Number Theme: _____

Astrological Sign: _____

Astrological Planet: _____

Mine: _____

_____

_____

INTERPRETATIONS

Fairfield: Defining and clarifying the identity. You are beginning to understand and see yourself more clearly. Defining new roles to play.

Noble: . . . communication and the joy of self-expression.

Greer: What are you envisioning for the future? What and with whom do you have to coordinate to achieve your plan?

Mine: _____

_____

_____

_____

THREE OF WANDS

NAMES FOR THE CARD

Traditional: _____Three of Cups_____

Alternatives: _____Bowls/Chalices/Vessels_____

_____

My Choice: _____

_____

SYMBOLS

Suit: _____

Number Theme: _____

Astrological Sign: _____

Astrological Planet: _____

Mine: _____

_____

_____

INTERPRETATIONS

Fairfield: Emotional or intuitive clarification. Naming your feelings or understanding an emotional pattern.

Noble: ... an expression of happiness and joyful time shared.... no threat from one another... sharing pleasure together, having fun with others.

Greer: What cause is there for celebration in your life?

Mine: _____

_____

_____

_____

THREE OF CUPS

3 ✝

♀

NAMES FOR THE CARD

Traditional: ___Three of Swords___

Alternatives: ___Crystals/Knives/Pens/Blades/Arrows___

_____

My Choice: _____

_____

SYMBOLS

Suit: _____

Number Theme: _____

Astrological Sign: _____

Astrological Planet: _____

Mine: _____

_____

_____

INTERPRETATIONS

Fairfield: Planning a philosophy or lifestyle. Clarifying and articulating what you think prior to presentation or publication.

Noble: The Three of Swords represents the way mental energies merge—through struggle.

Greer: In what ways are you suffering? Can you look at your relationships with truth and honesty?

Mine: _____

_____

_____

_____

THREE OF SWORDS

NAMES FOR THE CARD

Traditional: _____Three of Pentacles_____

Alternatives: _____Discs/Coins/Stars/Stones/Circles/Shields_____

_____

My Choice: _____

_____

SYMBOLS

Suit: _____

Number Theme: _____

Astrological Sign: _____

Astrological Planet: _____

Mine: _____

_____

_____

INTERPRETATIONS

Fairfield: Planning secure structures. Articulating the nature of material and financial security.

Noble: . . . work done together—a communal act of building.

Greer: How do you work with others? What skills are you using?

Mine: _____

_____

_____

_____

_____

THREE OF PENTACLES

NAMES FOR THE CARD

Traditional: _____Four of Wands_____

Alternatives: _____Rods/Staves/Pipes/Sticks/Scepters_____

_____

My Choice: _____

_____

SYMBOLS

Suit: _____

Number Theme: _____

Astrological Sign: _____

Astrological Planet: _____

Mine: _____

_____

_____

INTERPRETATIONS

Fairfield: Manifesting a new identity. Taking concrete steps toward putting the new you out into the world.

Noble: . . . a rite of passage . . . . passing from one stage of life to the next.

Greer: What role is ritual or ceremony playing in your life?

Mine: _____

_____

_____

_____

FOUR OF WANDS

NAMES FOR THE CARD

Traditional: ___Four of Cups___

Alternatives: ___Bowls/Chalices/Vessels___

_____

My Choice: _____

_____

SYMBOLS

Suit: _____

Number Theme: _____

Astrological Sign: _____

Astrological Planet: _____

Mine: _____

_____

_____

INTERPRETATIONS

Fairfield: Acting on what you feel. Doing something to express your emotions.

Noble: . . . a time for getting clear, refining things down to simple truth . . . . This time can be used for re-evaluation of life and relationships.

Greer: Where do you go to find peace and serenity?

Mine: _____

_____

_____

_____

FOUR OF CUPS

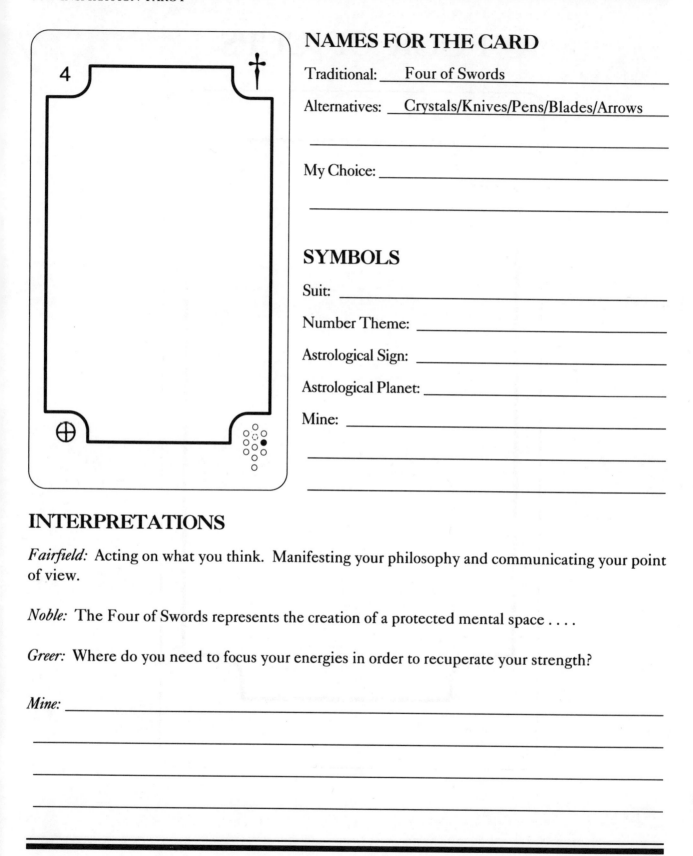

NAMES FOR THE CARD

Traditional: ___Four of Swords___

Alternatives: ___Crystals/Knives/Pens/Blades/Arrows___

_____

My Choice: _____

_____

SYMBOLS

Suit: _____

Number Theme: _____

Astrological Sign: _____

Astrological Planet: _____

Mine: _____

_____

_____

INTERPRETATIONS

Fairfield: Acting on what you think. Manifesting your philosophy and communicating your point of view.

Noble: The Four of Swords represents the creation of a protected mental space . . . .

Greer: Where do you need to focus your energies in order to recuperate your strength?

Mine: _____

_____

_____

_____

FOUR OF SWORDS

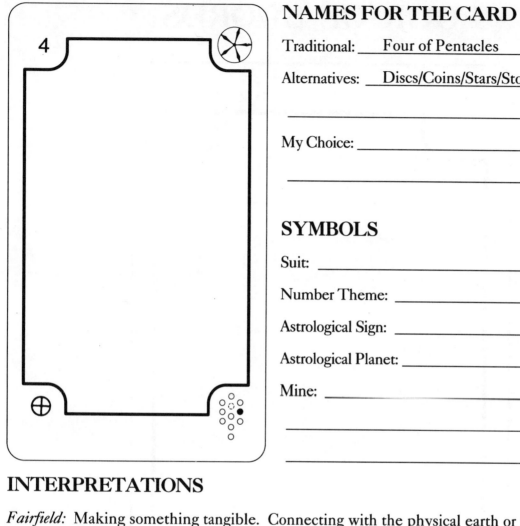

NAMES FOR THE CARD

Traditional: ___Four of Pentacles___

Alternatives: ___Discs/Coins/Stars/Stones/Circles/Shields___

_____

My Choice: _____

_____

SYMBOLS

Suit: _____

Number Theme: _____

Astrological Sign: _____

Astrological Planet: _____

Mine: _____

_____

_____

INTERPRETATIONS

Fairfield: Making something tangible. Connecting with the physical earth or taking other action related to feeling grounded or centered.

Noble: . . . an inner sanctuary of some kind, perhaps a room or house, where a person can be alone and sheltered . . . . the fourth [disc] promises integration of the four elements.

Greer: What is keeping you centered? What gives you a sense of security?

Mine: _____

_____

_____

_____

FOUR OF PENTACLES

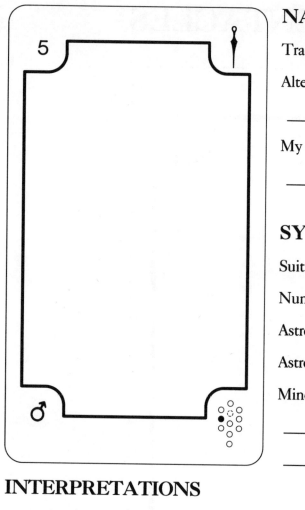

NAMES FOR THE CARD

Traditional: _____Five of Wands_____

Alternatives: _____Rods/Staves/Pipes/Sticks/Scepters_____

_____

My Choice: _____

_____

SYMBOLS

Suit: _____

Number Theme: _____

Astrological Sign: _____

Astrological Planet: _____

Mine: _____

_____

_____

INTERPRETATIONS

Fairfield: Adjusting the identity. You are being challenged to adapt and grow. You are adjusting the way you present yourself to others.

Noble: . . . struggle and strife without pain . . . . some conflict remains in need of resolution, but there is an agreement . . . that this struggle shall be fair, without curses or "stings."

Greer: What obstacles are you confronting? What games are you playing?

Mine: _____

_____

_____

_____

FIVE OF WANDS

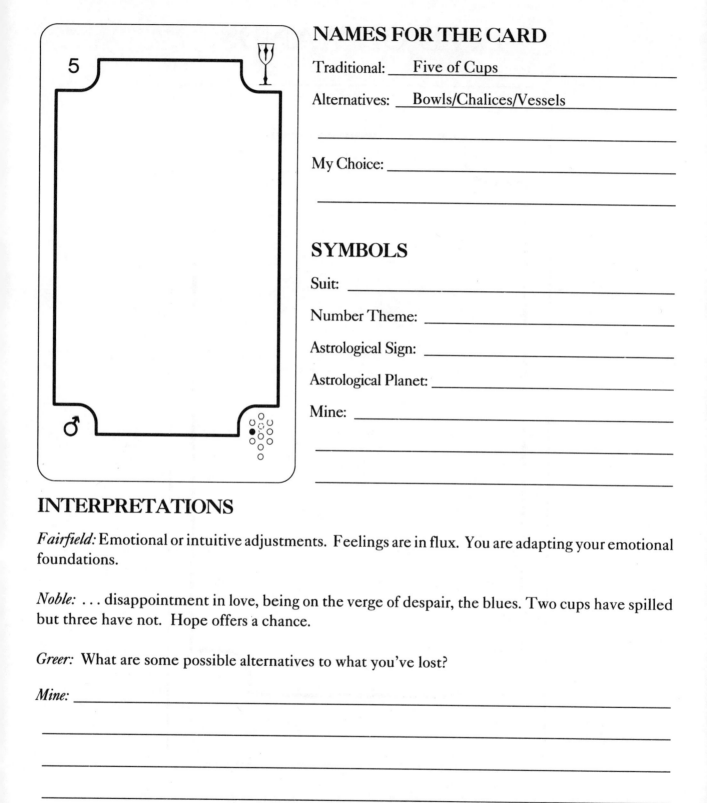

NAMES FOR THE CARD

Traditional: ___Five of Cups___

Alternatives: ___Bowls/Chalices/Vessels___

_____

My Choice: _____

_____

SYMBOLS

Suit: _____

Number Theme: _____

Astrological Sign: _____

Astrological Planet: _____

Mine: _____

_____

_____

INTERPRETATIONS

Fairfield: Emotional or intuitive adjustments. Feelings are in flux. You are adapting your emotional foundations.

Noble: . . . disappointment in love, being on the verge of despair, the blues. Two cups have spilled but three have not. Hope offers a chance.

Greer: What are some possible alternatives to what you've lost?

Mine: _____

_____

_____

_____

FIVE OF CUPS

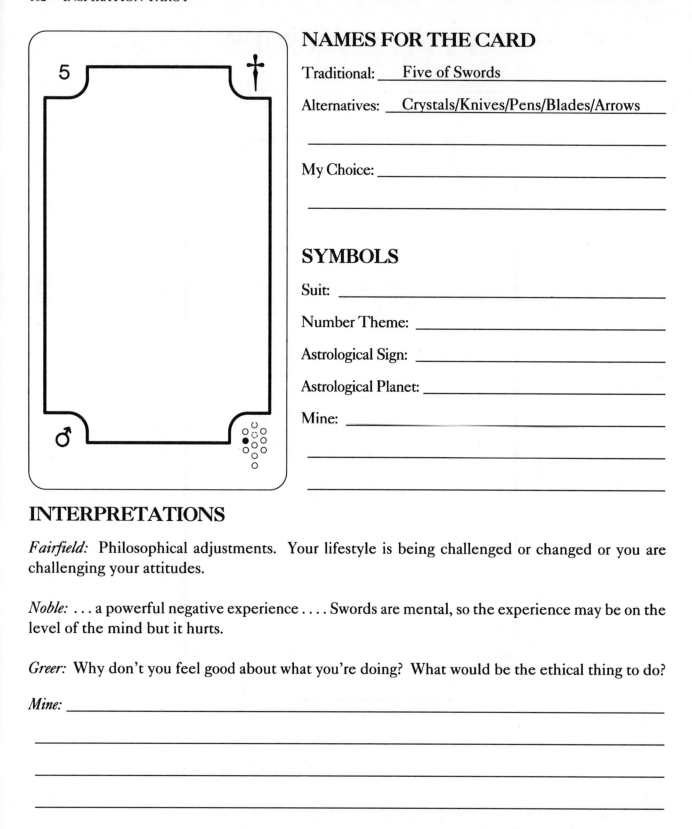

NAMES FOR THE CARD

Traditional: ___Five of Swords___

Alternatives: ___Crystals/Knives/Pens/Blades/Arrows___

_____

My Choice: _____

_____

SYMBOLS

Suit: _____

Number Theme: _____

Astrological Sign: _____

Astrological Planet: _____

Mine: _____

_____

_____

INTERPRETATIONS

Fairfield: Philosophical adjustments. Your lifestyle is being challenged or changed or you are challenging your attitudes.

Noble: . . . a powerful negative experience . . . . Swords are mental, so the experience may be on the level of the mind but it hurts.

Greer: Why don't you feel good about what you're doing? What would be the ethical thing to do?

Mine: _____

_____

_____

_____

FIVE OF SWORDS

```
  5                    ⊗



                              ♂                 ○
                                            ○ ○ ○
                                             ● ○ ○
                                             ○ ○
                                               ○
```

NAMES FOR THE CARD

Traditional: _____Five of Pentacles_____

Alternatives: ____Discs/Coins/Stars/Stones/Circles/Shields____

_____

My Choice: _____

_____

SYMBOLS

Suit: _____

Number Theme: _____

Astrological Sign: _____

Astrological Planet: _____

Mine: _____

_____

_____

INTERPRETATIONS

Fairfield: Physical adjustments. Your security is being changed or adjusted in some way.

Noble: . . . tension is held in the body . . . . Probably the mind is focused on survival issues . . . . Change is taking place but on the inside, not yet manifested.

Greer: What are you worried or anxious about? What conventions/traditions are you rebelling against?

Mine: _____

_____

_____

_____

FIVE OF PENTACLES

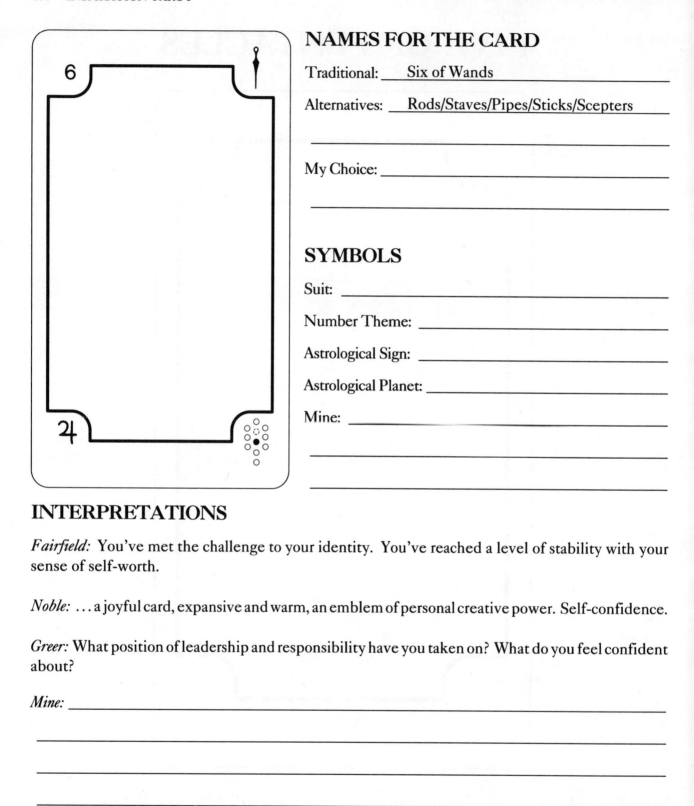

NAMES FOR THE CARD

Traditional: ___Six of Wands___

Alternatives: ___Rods/Staves/Pipes/Sticks/Scepters___

_____

My Choice: _____

_____

SYMBOLS

Suit: _____

Number Theme: _____

Astrological Sign: _____

Astrological Planet: _____

Mine: _____

_____

_____

INTERPRETATIONS

Fairfield: You've met the challenge to your identity. You've reached a level of stability with your sense of self-worth.

Noble: . . . a joyful card, expansive and warm, an emblem of personal creative power. Self-confidence.

Greer: What position of leadership and responsibility have you taken on? What do you feel confident about?

Mine: _____

_____

_____

_____

SIX OF WANDS

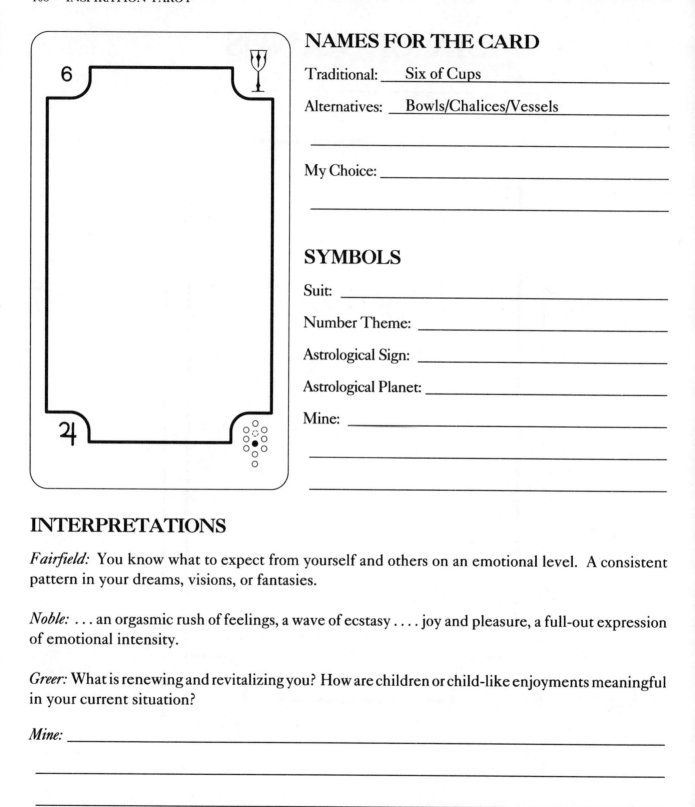

NAMES FOR THE CARD

Traditional: ___Six of Cups___

Alternatives: ___Bowls/Chalices/Vessels___

_____

My Choice: _____

_____

SYMBOLS

Suit: _____

Number Theme: _____

Astrological Sign: _____

Astrological Planet: _____

Mine: _____

_____

_____

INTERPRETATIONS

Fairfield: You know what to expect from yourself and others on an emotional level. A consistent pattern in your dreams, visions, or fantasies.

Noble: . . . an orgasmic rush of feelings, a wave of ecstasy . . . . joy and pleasure, a full-out expression of emotional intensity.

Greer: What is renewing and revitalizing you? How are children or child-like enjoyments meaningful in your current situation?

Mine: _____

_____

_____

SIX OF CUPS

NAMES FOR THE CARD

Traditional: ____Six of Swords____

Alternatives: ____Crystals/Knives/Pens/Blades/Arrows____

_____

My Choice: _____

_____

SYMBOLS

Suit: _____

Number Theme: _____

Astrological Sign: _____

Astrological Planet: _____

Mine: _____

_____

_____

INTERPRETATIONS

Fairfield: You're reintegrating your daily lifestyle, beliefs or attitudes after some challenge and confusion.

Noble: ... parts of the personality—come together at a central point.... perspective, getting distance, and taking care of hurt parts of the self.

Greer: Where in your life right now is mental clarity important? When you step back from your problem to gain perspective, what do you see?

Mine: _____

_____

_____

SIX OF SWORDS

NAMES FOR THE CARD

Traditional: ___Six of Pentacles___

Alternatives: ___Discs/Coins/Stars/Stones/Circles/Shields___

My Choice: _____

SYMBOLS

Suit: _____

Number Theme: _____

Astrological Sign: _____

Astrological Planet: _____

Mine: _____

INTERPRETATIONS

Fairfield: You are re-centering yourself and re-establishing your security base after a period of confusion or challenge.

Noble: ... generosity, having more than enough, sharing health and good fortune. A healing is taking place .... it is physical and tangible.

Greer: With whom are you sharing your prosperity, resources, or abilities?

Mine: _____

SIX OF PENTACLES

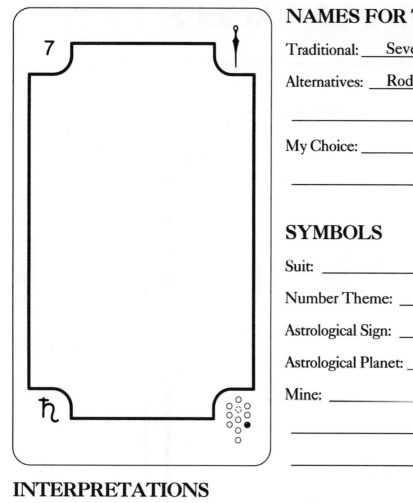

NAMES FOR THE CARD

Traditional: ___Seven of Wands___

Alternatives: ___Rods/Staves/Pipes/Sticks/Scepters___

_____

My Choice: _____

_____

SYMBOLS

Suit: _____

Number Theme: _____

Astrological Sign: _____

Astrological Planet: _____

Mine: _____

_____

_____

INTERPRETATIONS

Fairfield: Experimenting with different roles. Discovering many facets of your personality and expanding your interests.

Noble: . . . responsibility—the priestess of the Six . . . is now standing completely on her own and must trust herself to know how to handle the most difficult of situations.

Greer: How can you most effectively take a stand and present your point of view?

Mine: _____

_____

_____

_____

SEVEN OF WANDS

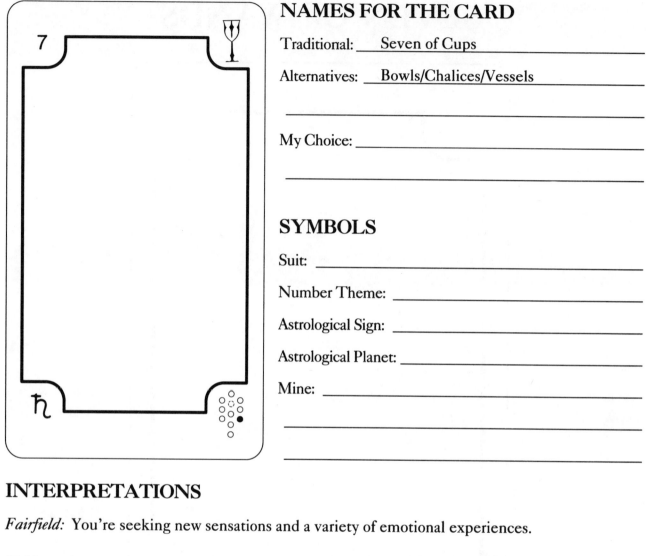

NAMES FOR THE CARD

Traditional: ___Seven of Cups___

Alternatives: ___Bowls/Chalices/Vessels___

_____

My Choice: _____

_____

SYMBOLS

Suit: _____

Number Theme: _____

Astrological Sign: _____

Astrological Planet: _____

Mine: _____

_____

_____

INTERPRETATIONS

Fairfield: You're seeking new sensations and a variety of emotional experiences.

Noble: . . . imagination and dreaminess, watery visions, fantasy . . . . choices, an abundance of them.

Greer: What are your fantasies for the future? What mystical or religious visions are you experiencing?

Mine: _____

_____

_____

_____

_____

SEVEN OF CUPS

NAMES FOR THE CARD

Traditional: ___Seven of Swords___

Alternatives: ___Crystals/Knives/Pens/Blades/Arrows___

_____

My Choice: _____

_____

SYMBOLS

Suit: _____

Number Theme: _____

Astrological Sign: _____

Astrological Planet: _____

Mine: _____

_____

_____

INTERPRETATIONS

Fairfield: You're experimenting with your schedule, lifestyle, daily routine, beliefs or attitudes.

Noble: ... mental strategy felt to be necessary after the detached clarity of the Six .... the mind creates a plan to get what it wants.

Greer: What is your strategy to achieve your ends? Do you trust the people you are working with?

Mine: _____

_____

_____

_____

SEVEN OF SWORDS

NAMES FOR THE CARD

Traditional: __Seven of Pentacles__

Alternatives: __Discs/Coins/Stars/Stones/Circles/Shields__

My Choice: _____

SYMBOLS

Suit: _____

Number Theme: _____

Astrological Sign: _____

Astrological Planet: _____

Mine: _____

INTERPRETATIONS

Fairfield: You are experimenting with money, material resources, or your body in a variety of ways in which you could feel centered, safe and grounded.

Noble: . . . a representation of growth and waiting . . . . trusting that the idea is taking form, a thinker must wait.

Greer: What is growing and maturing that you are concerned about? What mistakes did you make in the past in similar circumstances and what can you do differently now?

Mine: _____

SEVEN OF PENTACLES

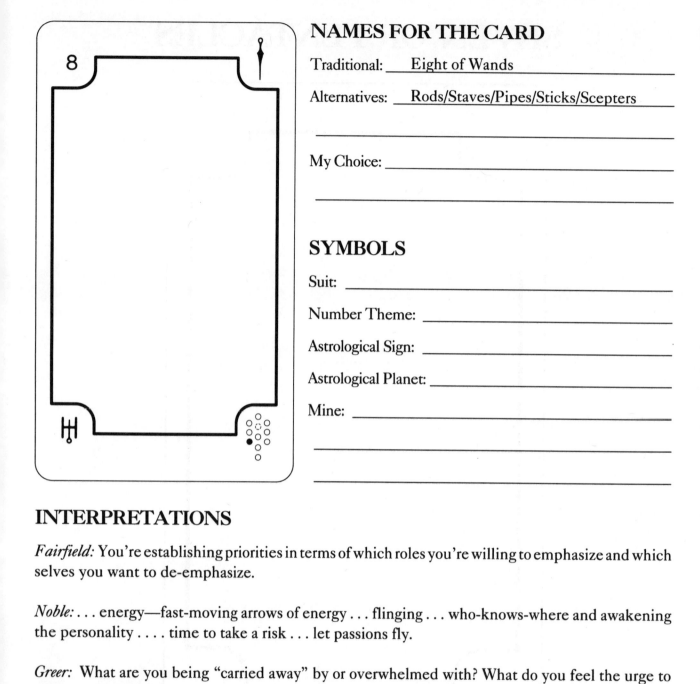

NAMES FOR THE CARD

Traditional: ___Eight of Wands___

Alternatives: ___Rods/Staves/Pipes/Sticks/Scepters___

_____

My Choice: _____

_____

SYMBOLS

Suit: _____

Number Theme: _____

Astrological Sign: _____

Astrological Planet: _____

Mine: _____

_____

_____

INTERPRETATIONS

Fairfield: You're establishing priorities in terms of which roles you're willing to emphasize and which selves you want to de-emphasize.

Noble: . . . energy—fast-moving arrows of energy . . . flinging . . . who-knows-where and awakening the personality . . . . time to take a risk . . . let passions fly.

Greer: What are you being "carried away" by or overwhelmed with? What do you feel the urge to move on quickly?

Mine: _____

_____

_____

EIGHT OF WANDS

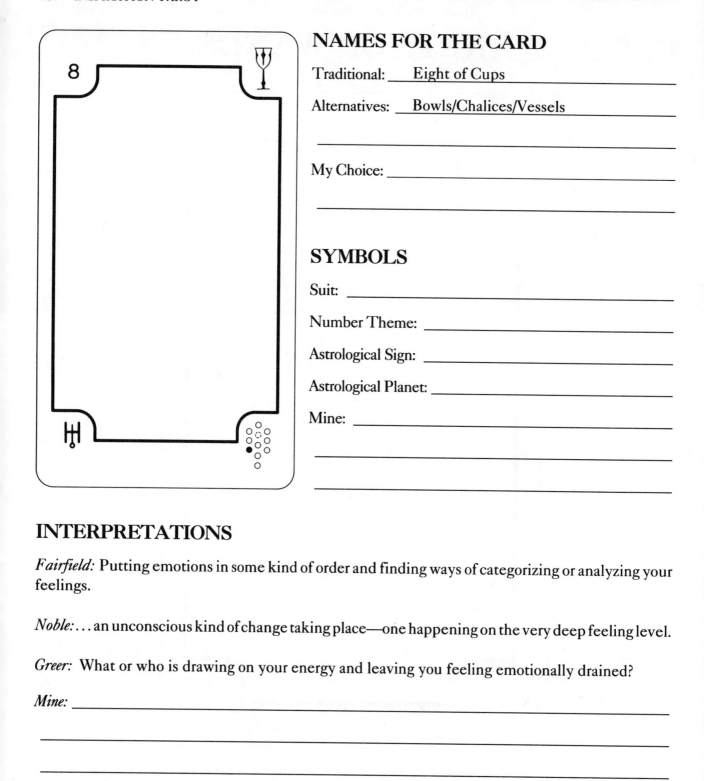

NAMES FOR THE CARD

Traditional: ___Eight of Cups___

Alternatives: ___Bowls/Chalices/Vessels___

___

My Choice: ___

___

SYMBOLS

Suit: ___

Number Theme: ___

Astrological Sign: ___

Astrological Planet: ___

Mine: ___

___

___

INTERPRETATIONS

Fairfield: Putting emotions in some kind of order and finding ways of categorizing or analyzing your feelings.

Noble: ... an unconscious kind of change taking place—one happening on the very deep feeling level.

Greer: What or who is drawing on your energy and leaving you feeling emotionally drained?

Mine: ___

___

___

___

EIGHT OF CUPS

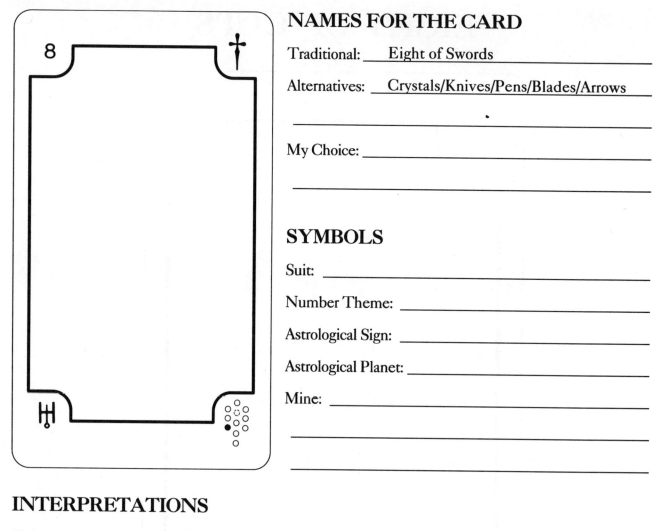

NAMES FOR THE CARD

Traditional: __Eight of Swords__

Alternatives: __Crystals/Knives/Pens/Blades/Arrows__

_____

My Choice: _____

_____

SYMBOLS

Suit: _____

Number Theme: _____

Astrological Sign: _____

Astrological Planet: _____

Mine: _____

_____

_____

INTERPRETATIONS

Fairfield: . . . actively organizing your lifestyle, activities, beliefs or attitudes and finding ways to match your values more closely.

Noble: . . . the activity of fighting one's way out of a box created by the mind . . . . indecision and a feeling that things are working against one.

Greer: What would you do if you could get rid of the obstacles and blocks? What is interfering with your creative expression?

Mine: _____

_____

_____

EIGHT OF SWORDS

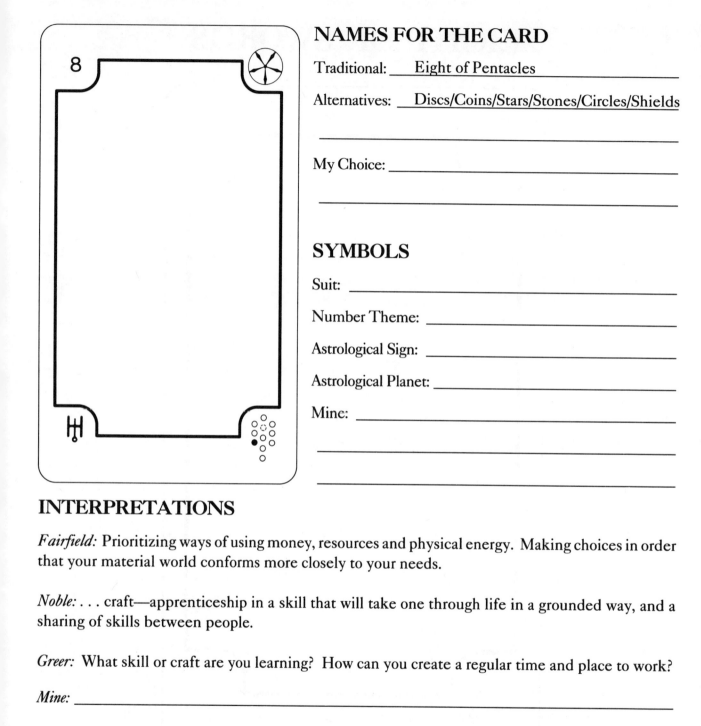

NAMES FOR THE CARD

Traditional: ___Eight of Pentacles___

Alternatives: ___Discs/Coins/Stars/Stones/Circles/Shields___

_____

My Choice: _____

_____

SYMBOLS

Suit: _____

Number Theme: _____

Astrological Sign: _____

Astrological Planet: _____

Mine: _____

_____

_____

INTERPRETATIONS

Fairfield: Prioritizing ways of using money, resources and physical energy. Making choices in order that your material world conforms more closely to your needs.

Noble: . . . craft—apprenticeship in a skill that will take one through life in a grounded way, and a sharing of skills between people.

Greer: What skill or craft are you learning? How can you create a regular time and place to work?

Mine: _____

_____

_____

_____

EIGHT OF PENTACLES

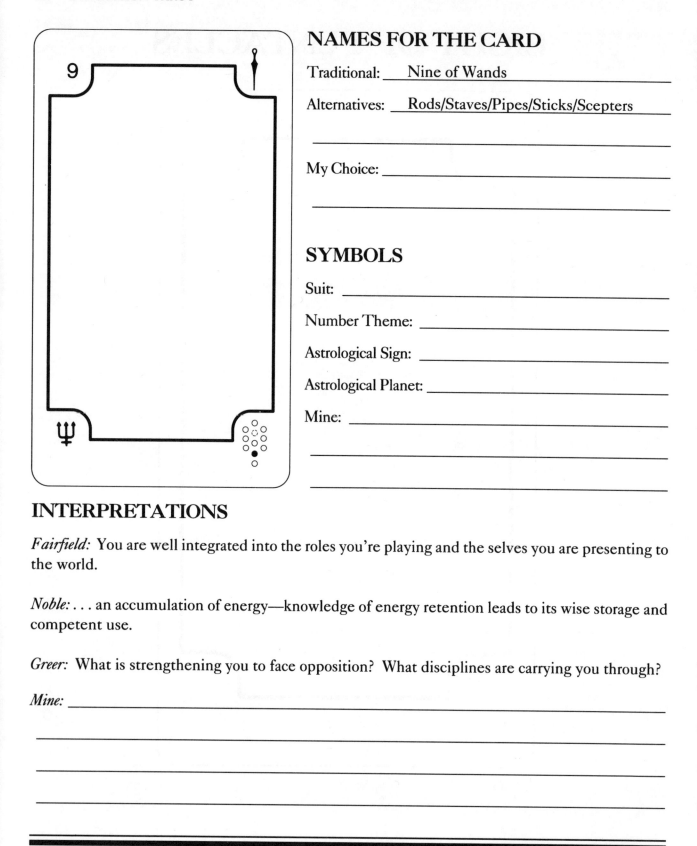

NAMES FOR THE CARD

Traditional: ___Nine of Wands___

Alternatives: ___Rods/Staves/Pipes/Sticks/Scepters___

_____

My Choice: _____

_____

SYMBOLS

Suit: _____

Number Theme: _____

Astrological Sign: _____

Astrological Planet: _____

Mine: _____

_____

_____

INTERPRETATIONS

Fairfield: You are well integrated into the roles you're playing and the selves you are presenting to the world.

Noble: . . . an accumulation of energy—knowledge of energy retention leads to its wise storage and competent use.

Greer: What is strengthening you to face opposition? What disciplines are carrying you through?

Mine: _____

_____

_____

_____

NINE OF WANDS

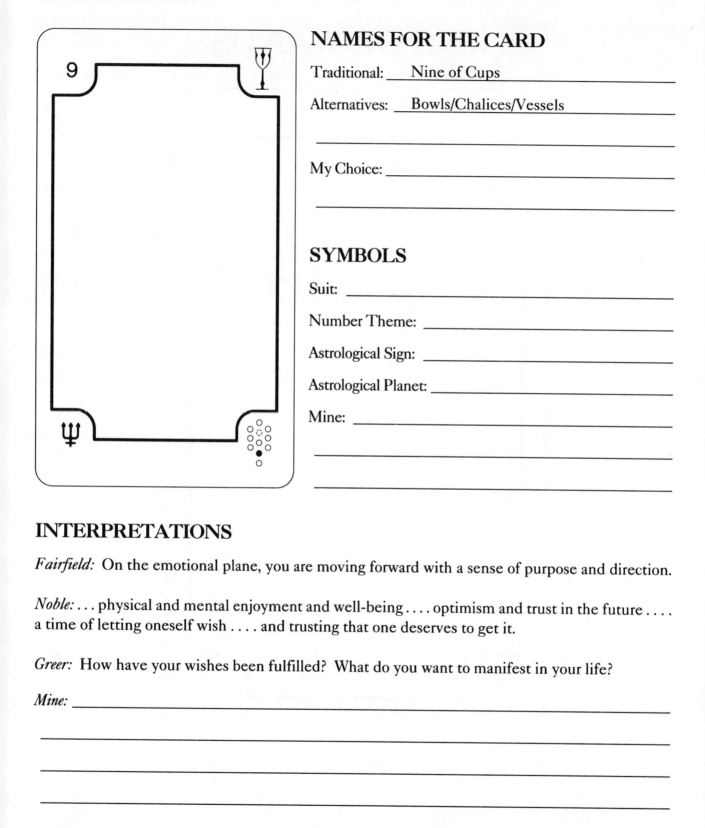

NAMES FOR THE CARD

Traditional: ___Nine of Cups___

Alternatives: ___Bowls/Chalices/Vessels___

_____

My Choice: _____

_____

SYMBOLS

Suit: _____

Number Theme: _____

Astrological Sign: _____

Astrological Planet: _____

Mine: _____

_____

_____

INTERPRETATIONS

Fairfield: On the emotional plane, you are moving forward with a sense of purpose and direction.

Noble: . . . physical and mental enjoyment and well-being . . . . optimism and trust in the future . . . . a time of letting oneself wish . . . . and trusting that one deserves to get it.

Greer: How have your wishes been fulfilled? What do you want to manifest in your life?

Mine: _____

_____

_____

_____

NINE OF CUPS

NAMES FOR THE CARD

Traditional: __Nine of Swords__

Alternatives: __Crystals/Knives/Pens/Blades/Arrows__

_____

My Choice: _____

_____

SYMBOLS

Suit: _____

Number Theme: _____

Astrological Sign: _____

Astrological Planet: _____

Mine: _____

_____

_____

INTERPRETATIONS

Fairfield: Your lifestyle or daily schedule is proceeding smoothly. Your attitudes and opinions are well-integrated within yourself.

Noble: ... the rising up from the unconscious of all the fears and projections the mind has made during its process of thought.

Greer: What is the source of your depression? What can you do to improve the situation?

Mine: _____

_____

_____

_____

NINE OF SWORDS

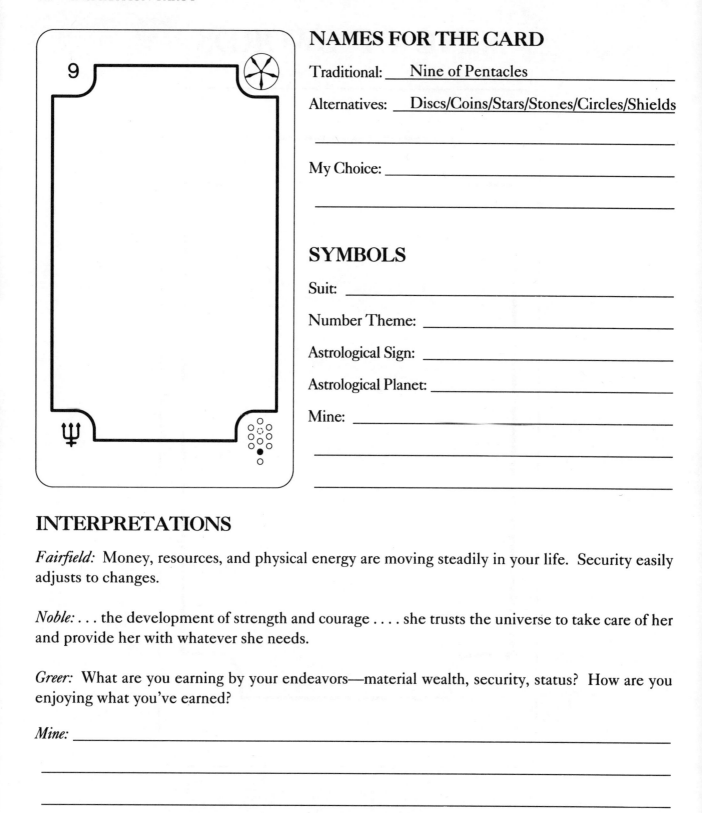

NAMES FOR THE CARD

Traditional: ___Nine of Pentacles___

Alternatives: ___Discs/Coins/Stars/Stones/Circles/Shields___

My Choice: _____

SYMBOLS

Suit: _____

Number Theme: _____

Astrological Sign: _____

Astrological Planet: _____

Mine: _____

INTERPRETATIONS

Fairfield: Money, resources, and physical energy are moving steadily in your life. Security easily adjusts to changes.

Noble: . . . the development of strength and courage . . . . she trusts the universe to take care of her and provide her with whatever she needs.

Greer: What are you earning by your endeavors—material wealth, security, status? How are you enjoying what you've earned?

Mine: _____

NINE OF PENTACLES

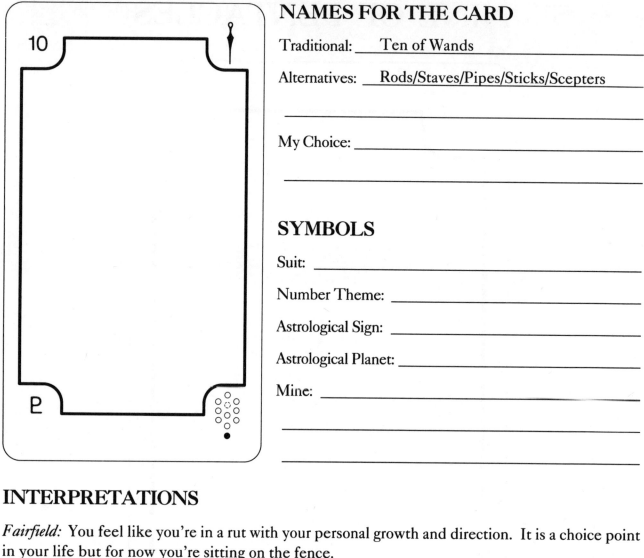

NAMES FOR THE CARD

Traditional: _____Ten of Wands_____

Alternatives: _____Rods/Staves/Pipes/Sticks/Scepters_____

_____

My Choice: _____

_____

SYMBOLS

Suit: _____

Number Theme: _____

Astrological Sign: _____

Astrological Planet: _____

Mine: _____

_____

_____

INTERPRETATIONS

Fairfield: You feel like you're in a rut with your personal growth and direction. It is a choice point in your life but for now you're sitting on the fence.

Noble: . . . a release of all the energies that have built up over time . . . that now and then overwhelm the personality.

Greer: What responsibilities are weighing heavily on your shoulders? How can you best use your powers and energies?

Mine: _____

_____

_____

TEN OF WANDS

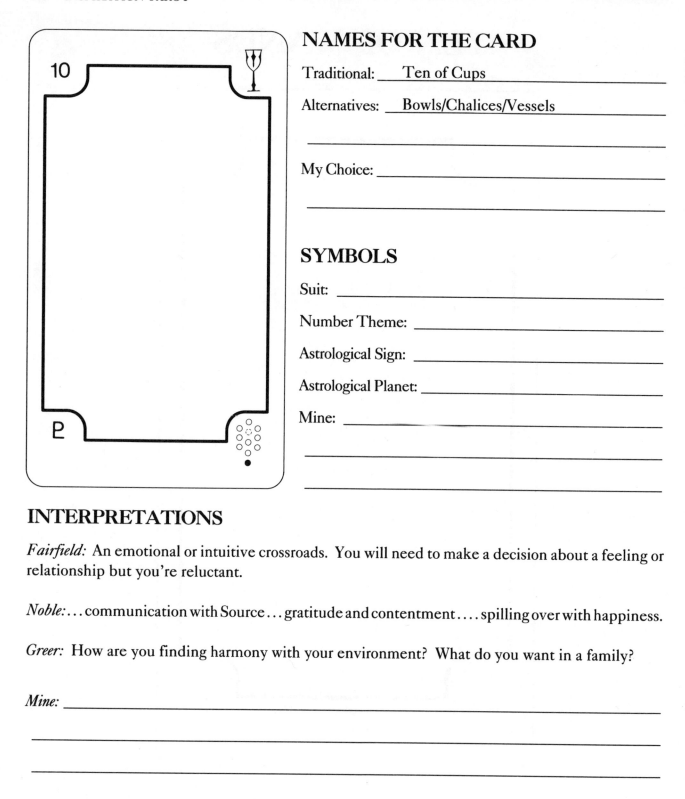

NAMES FOR THE CARD

Traditional: ___Ten of Cups___

Alternatives: ___Bowls/Chalices/Vessels___

_____

My Choice: _____

_____

SYMBOLS

Suit: _____

Number Theme: _____

Astrological Sign: _____

Astrological Planet: _____

Mine: _____

_____

_____

INTERPRETATIONS

Fairfield: An emotional or intuitive crossroads. You will need to make a decision about a feeling or relationship but you're reluctant.

Noble: ... communication with Source ... gratitude and contentment .... spilling over with happiness.

Greer: How are you finding harmony with your environment? What do you want in a family?

Mine: _____

_____

_____

_____

TEN OF CUPS

NAMES FOR THE CARD

Traditional: ___Ten of Swords___

Alternatives: ___Crystals/Knives/Pens/Blades/Arrows___

_____

My Choice: _____

_____

SYMBOLS

Suit: _____

Number Theme: _____

Astrological Sign: _____

Astrological Planet: _____

Mine: _____

_____

_____

INTERPRETATIONS

Fairfield: The process of making some decisions regarding lifestyle, schedule, daily routine, communications, beliefs, attitudes, or values, but you're not ready to complete the choices and move on.

Noble: . . . the final letting go of some idea to which the ego has been attached . . . . abandonment of a cherished image, plan or way of life.

Greer: By totally accepting defeat, what are you now free to do?

Mine: _____

_____

_____

TEN OF SWORDS

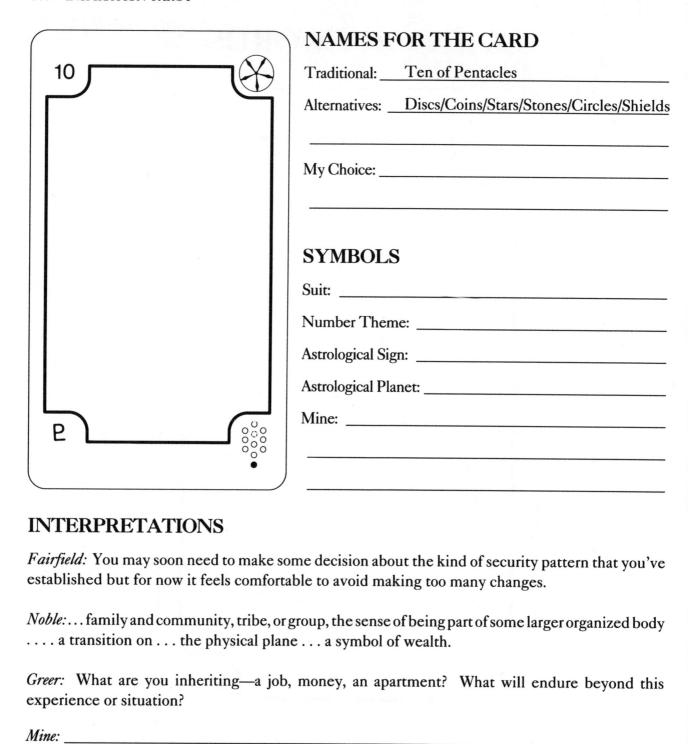

NAMES FOR THE CARD

Traditional: ___Ten of Pentacles___

Alternatives: ___Discs/Coins/Stars/Stones/Circles/Shields___

_____

My Choice: _____

_____

SYMBOLS

Suit: _____

Number Theme: _____

Astrological Sign: _____

Astrological Planet: _____

Mine: _____

_____

_____

INTERPRETATIONS

Fairfield: You may soon need to make some decision about the kind of security pattern that you've established but for now it feels comfortable to avoid making too many changes.

Noble: ... family and community, tribe, or group, the sense of being part of some larger organized body . . . . a transition on . . . the physical plane . . . a symbol of wealth.

Greer: What are you inheriting—a job, money, an apartment? What will endure beyond this experience or situation?

Mine: _____

_____

_____

TEN OF PENTACLES

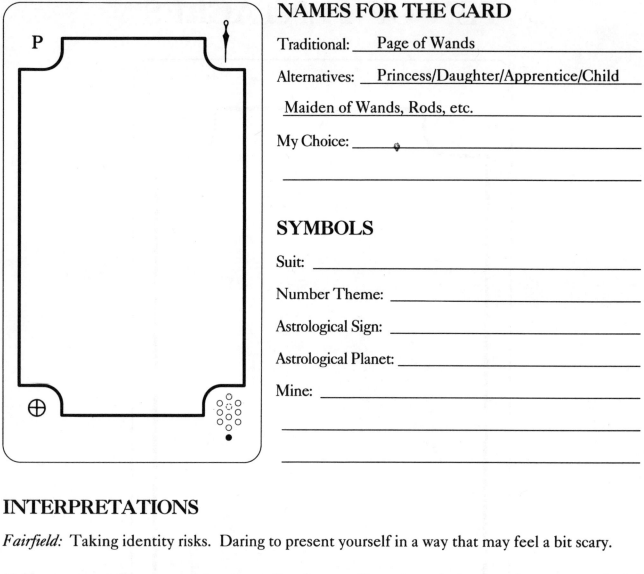

NAMES FOR THE CARD

Traditional: ___Page of Wands___

Alternatives: ___Princess/Daughter/Apprentice/Child___

___Maiden of Wands, Rods, etc.___

My Choice: _____

_____

SYMBOLS

Suit: _____

Number Theme: _____

Astrological Sign: _____

Astrological Planet: _____

Mine: _____

_____

_____

INTERPRETATIONS

Fairfield: Taking identity risks. Daring to present yourself in a way that may feel a bit scary.

Noble: . . . young, fiery part of the personality that manifests through dance and movement, joyful change, and growth . . . . natural joy within you bursting free in some way.

Greer: What new territories and ideas are you checking out? What actions are you risking to take?

Mine: _____

_____

_____

_____

PAGE OF WANDS

NAMES FOR THE CARD

Traditional: ___Page of Cups___

Alternatives: ___Princess/Daughter/Apprentice/Child___

___Maiden of Cups, Bowls, etc.___

My Choice: _____

_____

SYMBOLS

Suit: _____

Number Theme: _____

Astrological Sign: _____

Astrological Planet: _____

Mine: _____

_____

_____

INTERPRETATIONS

Fairfield: Emotional risk taking. You've chosen to jump in and commit to an emotional direction or relationship even though you're not sure where it will lead.

Noble: . . . experiencing your feelings very strongly . . . . the process of experiencing them is what counts . . . . Take a break—respect your feelings and your senses.

Greer: What does your intuition say to do?

Mine: _____

_____

_____

_____

PAGE OF CUPS

P † ⊕

NAMES FOR THE CARD

Traditional: ___Page of Swords___

Alternatives: ___Princess/Daughter/Apprentice/Child___

___Maiden of Swords, Knives, etc.___

My Choice: _____

_____

SYMBOLS

Suit: _____

Number Theme: _____

Astrological Sign: _____

Astrological Planet: _____

Mine: _____

_____

_____

INTERPRETATIONS

Fairfield: Risks in thoughts or lifestyle. You're willing to take risks to actively pursue and manifest a philosophy or value system that's important to you.

Noble: . . . the urge to action, impulsive and rash . . . . a time of activity and starting new projects. What you want you want right now!

Greer: What do you have to say? What fears must you face?

Mine: _____

_____

_____

_____

PAGE OF SWORDS

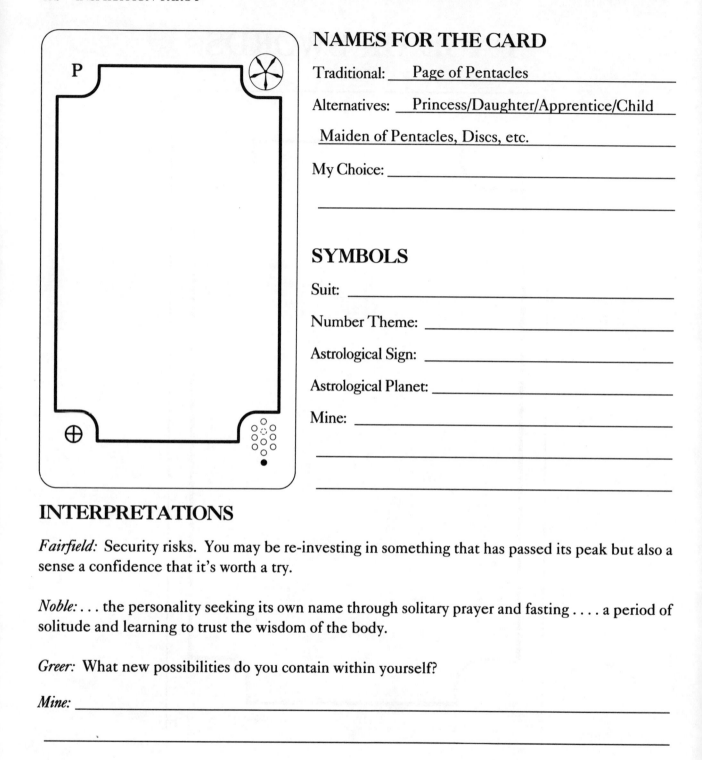

NAMES FOR THE CARD

Traditional: ___Page of Pentacles___

Alternatives: ___Princess/Daughter/Apprentice/Child___

___Maiden of Pentacles, Discs, etc.___

My Choice: _____

_____

SYMBOLS

Suit: _____

Number Theme: _____

Astrological Sign: _____

Astrological Planet: _____

Mine: _____

_____

_____

INTERPRETATIONS

Fairfield: Security risks. You may be re-investing in something that has passed its peak but also a sense a confidence that it's worth a try.

Noble: . . . the personality seeking its own name through solitary prayer and fasting . . . . a period of solitude and learning to trust the wisdom of the body.

Greer: What new possibilities do you contain within yourself?

Mine: _____

_____

_____

_____

PAGE OF PENTACLES

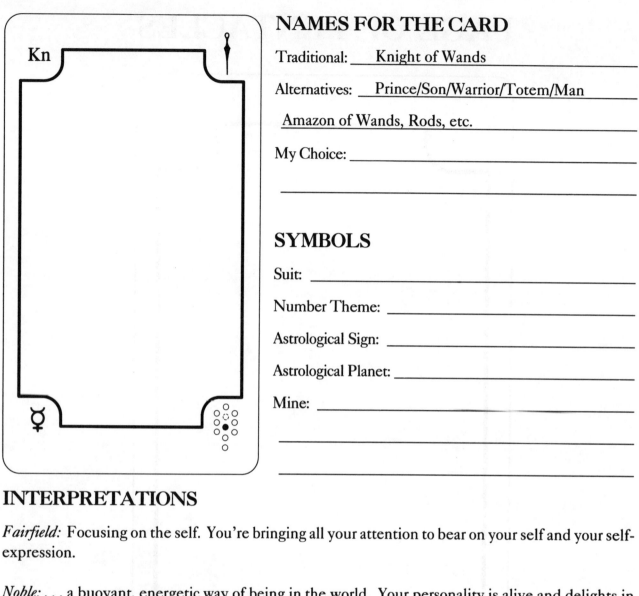

NAMES FOR THE CARD

Traditional: ___Knight of Wands___

Alternatives: ___Prince/Son/Warrior/Totem/Man___

___Amazon of Wands, Rods, etc.___

My Choice: _____

_____

SYMBOLS

Suit: _____

Number Theme: _____

Astrological Sign: _____

Astrological Planet: _____

Mine: _____

_____

_____

INTERPRETATIONS

Fairfield: Focusing on the self. You're bringing all your attention to bear on your self and your self-expression.

Noble: . . . a buoyant, energetic way of being in the world. Your personality is alive and delights in amusing, entertaining and attracting others.

Greer: How are you . . . radiating creative or sexual energy in your life?

Mine: _____

_____

_____

_____

KNIGHT OF WANDS

NAMES FOR THE CARD

Traditional: ___Knight of Cups___

Alternatives: ___Prince/Son/Warrior/Totem/Man___

___Amazon of Cups, Bowls, etc.___

My Choice: _____

_____

SYMBOLS

Suit: _____

Number Theme: _____

Astrological Sign: _____

Astrological Planet: _____

Mine: _____

_____

_____

INTERPRETATIONS

Fairfield: Emotional or intuitive focus. You're so involved in this feeling or relationship that everything else seems insignificant by comparison.

Noble: ... the quiet, inner aspect of the male principle .... it points to self-reflection and peaceful, meditative awareness. Your mind turns to artistic visions or recognizes deep feelings.

Greer: What dream, vision, ideal or love are you following?

Mine: _____

_____

_____

_____

KNIGHT OF CUPS

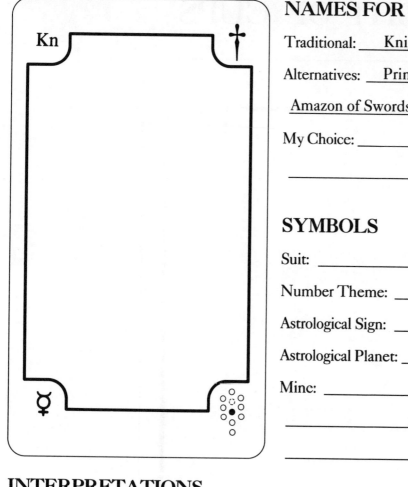

NAMES FOR THE CARD

Traditional: ___Knight of Swords___

Alternatives: ___Prince/Son/Warrior/Totem/Man___

___Amazon of Swords, Knives, etc.___

My Choice: _____

_____

SYMBOLS

Suit: _____

Number Theme: _____

Astrological Sign: _____

Astrological Planet: _____

Minc: _____

_____

_____

INTERPRETATIONS

Fairfield: Philosophical focus. You are so involved with the pattern of your daily routine that everything else seems to recede in importance.

Noble: . . . you are approaching your goals in an overly rational way . . . . your ego is about to strangle the dove of your heart . . . . Let go of the false sense of isolation you feel and connect with the rest of life.

Greer: What point do you feel committed to make?

Mine: _____

_____

_____

KNIGHT OF SWORDS

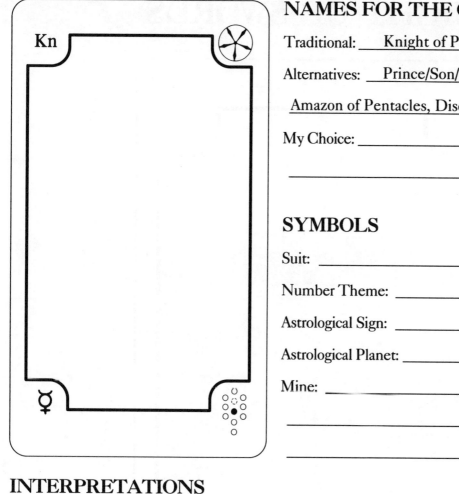

NAMES FOR THE CARD

Traditional: ___Knight of Pentacles___

Alternatives: ___Prince/Son/Warrior/Totem/Man___

___Amazon of Pentacles, Discs, etc.___

My Choice: _____

_____

SYMBOLS

Suit: _____

Number Theme: _____

Astrological Sign: _____

Astrological Planet: _____

Mine: _____

_____

_____

INTERPRETATIONS

Fairfield: Focused in the material world. You are focusing so hard on establishing security that nothing else seems relevant.

Noble: . . . the archetypal hunter, the male principle embodied in a seeker . . . . you are working steadily towards your goals. You know what it is that you want, and you hold a one-pointed focus on getting it.

Greer: How are you . . . committed to security and conventions?

Mine: _____

_____

_____

KNIGHT OF PENTACLES

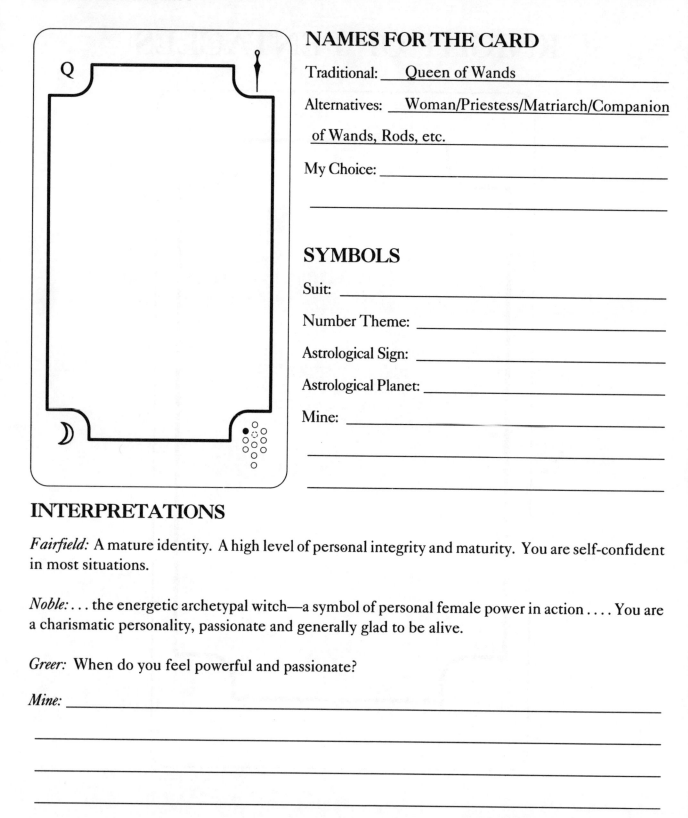

NAMES FOR THE CARD

Traditional: ___Queen of Wands___

Alternatives: ___Woman/Priestess/Matriarch/Companion___

___of Wands, Rods, etc.___

My Choice: _____

_____

SYMBOLS

Suit: _____

Number Theme: _____

Astrological Sign: _____

Astrological Planet: _____

Mine: _____

_____

_____

INTERPRETATIONS

Fairfield: A mature identity. A high level of personal integrity and maturity. You are self-confident in most situations.

Noble: . . . the energetic archetypal witch—a symbol of personal female power in action . . . . You are a charismatic personality, passionate and generally glad to be alive.

Greer: When do you feel powerful and passionate?

Mine: _____

_____

_____

_____

QUEEN OF WANDS

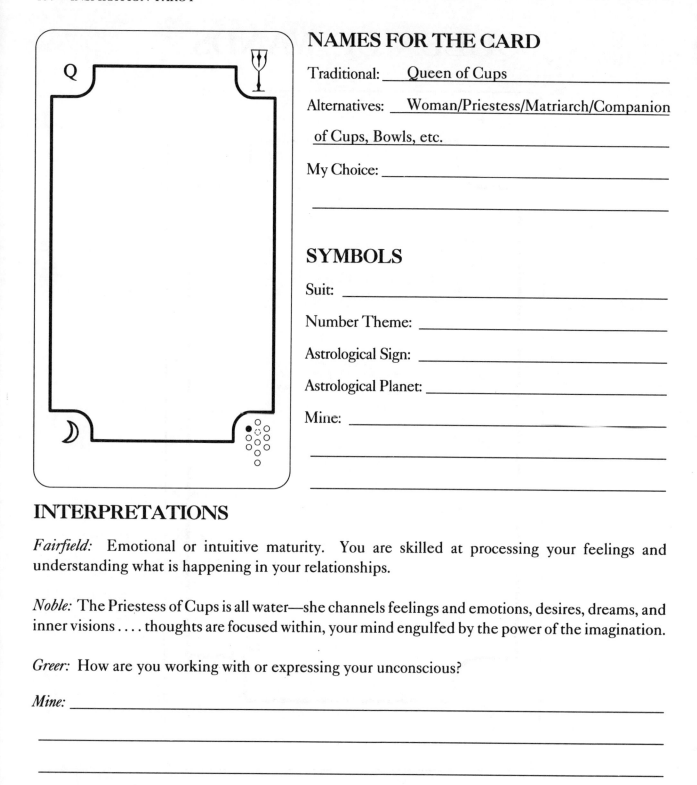

NAMES FOR THE CARD

Traditional: ___Queen of Cups___

Alternatives: ___Woman/Priestess/Matriarch/Companion___

___of Cups, Bowls, etc.___

My Choice: _____

_____

SYMBOLS

Suit: _____

Number Theme: _____

Astrological Sign: _____

Astrological Planet: _____

Mine: _____

_____

_____

INTERPRETATIONS

Fairfield: Emotional or intuitive maturity. You are skilled at processing your feelings and understanding what is happening in your relationships.

Noble: The Priestess of Cups is all water—she channels feelings and emotions, desires, dreams, and inner visions . . . . thoughts are focused within, your mind engulfed by the power of the imagination.

Greer: How are you working with or expressing your unconscious?

Mine: _____

_____

_____

_____

QUEEN OF CUPS

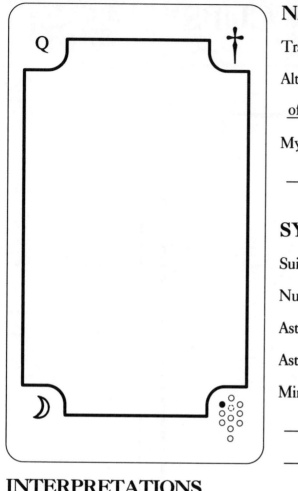

NAMES FOR THE CARD

Traditional: __Queen of Swords__

Alternatives: __Woman/Priestess/Matriarch/Companion__
__of Swords, Knives, etc.__

My Choice: _____

_____

SYMBOLS

Suit: _____

Number Theme: _____

Astrological Sign: _____

Astrological Planet: _____

Mine: _____

_____

_____

INTERPRETATIONS

Fairfield: Intellectual maturity. You are expressing your philosophy, fully and powerfully, through your lifestyles and activities.

Noble: . . . this card . . . suggests a journey to the cool realms of intellect, a time-out from the emotions in favor of a thoughtful, introspective period.

Greer: How are you being discriminating and analytical?

Mine: _____

_____

_____

_____

QUEEN OF SWORDS

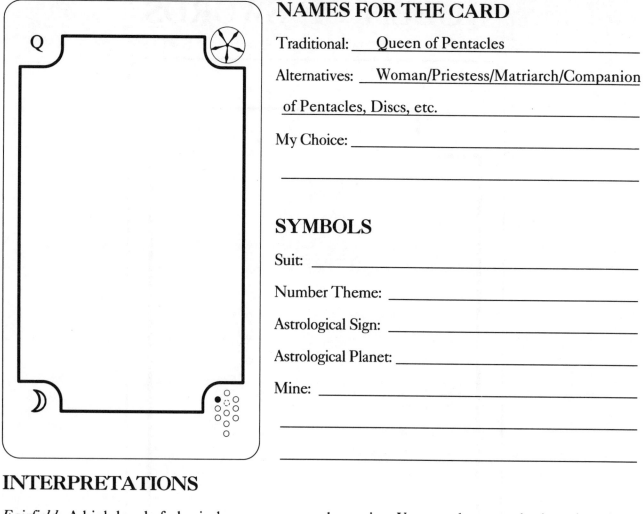

NAMES FOR THE CARD

Traditional: ___Queen of Pentacles___

Alternatives: ___Woman/Priestess/Matriarch/Companion___

___of Pentacles, Discs, etc.___

My Choice: _____

_____

SYMBOLS

Suit: _____

Number Theme: _____

Astrological Sign: _____

Astrological Planet: _____

Mine: _____

_____

_____

INTERPRETATIONS

Fairfield: A high level of physical competence and security. You may have reached a point where a particular pattern of health has become integrated into your body.

Noble: . . . the procreative and nurturing aspects of physical mothering . . . . a personality grounded in the physical world, in harmony with the slowed-down energies of Mother Nature.

Greer: How are you channeling your physical resources? How are you grounded in Mother Earth?

Mine: _____

_____

_____

_____

QUEEN OF PENTACLES

NAMES FOR THE CARD

Traditional: ___King of Wands___

Alternatives: ___Man/Shaman/Sage/Exemplar/Chief___

___Mother of Wands, Rods, etc.___

My Choice: _____

_____

SYMBOLS

Suit: _____

Number Theme: _____

Astrological Sign: _____

Astrological Planet: _____

Mine: _____

_____

_____

INTERPRETATIONS

Fairfield: Releasing an old identity. The end of a phase of personal development.

Noble: . . . positive male power . . . . a powerful personality capable of accomplishing long-term goals and handling extremely complex situations . . . . upright, it indicates no abuse of power.

Greer: Who do you admire for their sense of self?

Mine: _____

_____

_____

_____

KING OF WANDS

K

♂

NAMES FOR THE CARD

Traditional: ___King of Cups___

Alternatives: ___Man/Shaman/Sage/Exemplar/Chief___

___Mother of Cups, Bowls, etc.___

My Choice: _____

_____

SYMBOLS

Suit: _____

Number Theme: _____

Astrological Sign: _____

Astrological Planet: _____

Mine: _____

_____

_____

INTERPRETATIONS

Fairfield: Releasing an emotional pattern. An emotion has run its course and is no longer operative in your life.

Noble: . . . the Shaman of Cups represents feelings under control, passion transmuted into detached and focused awareness . . . . You know how to pull all your energies into facing the task at hand.

Greer: What feelings are you keeping under firm control?

Mine: _____

_____

_____

_____

KING OF CUPS

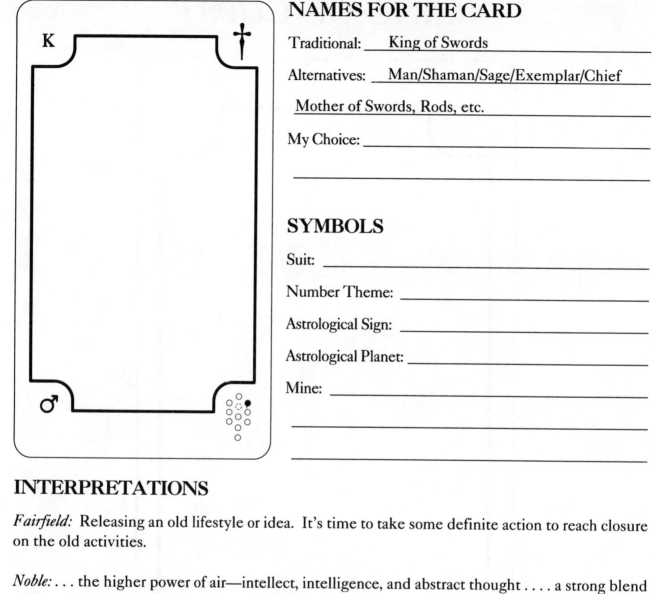

NAMES FOR THE CARD

Traditional: ___King of Swords___

Alternatives: ___Man/Shaman/Sage/Exemplar/Chief___

___Mother of Swords, Rods, etc.___

My Choice: _____

_____

SYMBOLS

Suit: _____

Number Theme: _____

Astrological Sign: _____

Astrological Planet: _____

Mine: _____

_____

_____

INTERPRETATIONS

Fairfield: Releasing an old lifestyle or idea. It's time to take some definite action to reach closure on the old activities.

Noble: . . . the higher power of air—intellect, intelligence, and abstract thought . . . . a strong blend of fiery ("female") emotions and powerful ("male") thought . . . . you have the power to transform reality.

Greer: How are you using your ability to be rational, logical and analytical?

Mine: _____

_____

_____

KING OF SWORDS

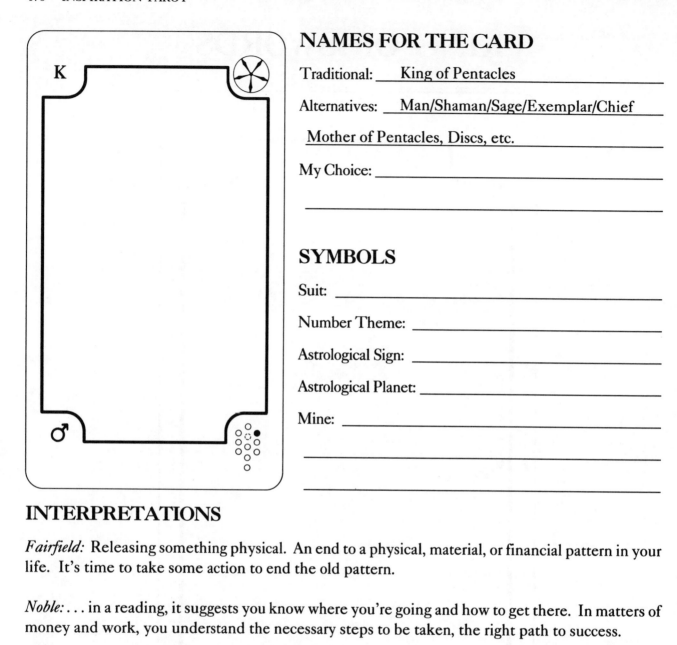

NAMES FOR THE CARD

Traditional: ___King of Pentacles___

Alternatives: ___Man/Shaman/Sage/Exemplar/Chief___

___Mother of Pentacles, Discs, etc.___

My Choice: _____

_____

SYMBOLS

Suit: _____

Number Theme: _____

Astrological Sign: _____

Astrological Planet: _____

Mine: _____

_____

_____

INTERPRETATIONS

Fairfield: Releasing something physical. An end to a physical, material, or financial pattern in your life. It's time to take some action to end the old pattern.

Noble: . . . in a reading, it suggests you know where you're going and how to get there. In matters of money and work, you understand the necessary steps to be taken, the right path to success.

Greer: How are you channeling your physical resources?

Mine: _____

_____

_____

_____

KING OF PENTACLES

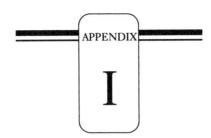

A Guided Relaxation Technique

The following is a suggested script you can use to create a light trance state. You may choose to either record the script yourself for use at a later time when you want to do some private imagery work, or you might ask a friend to read it aloud.

Each time you listen to the script you will want to seat yourself comfortably at a table or writing surface with some paper and drawing utensils. Make sure that your clothing and your seat are comfortable and supportive. Adjust the lighting or sound level around you until it is just right for you. Make sure that you are ready.

(BEGIN: Read slowly.) Take a few deep breaths and let your whole body feel the air moving in and out. As you breathe, let your concentration come into your body so that all your other concerns and interests fly away. With each out-breath, release your concerns; with each in-breath, focus on your body.

(SLOWLY)
OUT—release
IN—focus on your body
OUT—release
IN—focus on your body

Now, as you continue to breathe, allow your attention to come inside your body, into the center of your being, into the place where you *know* what you know. Release any physical tension and come toward your center.

(SLOWLY)
OUT—release
IN—come toward your center
OUT—release
IN—come toward your center

As you move deeper and deeper into the center of your being, allow your mind to remain alert and alive, awake to what you will soon discover.

While listening to the count, from ten to one, relax your body as your attention becomes more and more focused.

(PAUSE BETWEEN THE NUMBERS)
TEN—relax and release
NINE—focus your attention within your consciousness
EIGHT—move deeper and deeper
SEVEN—feel the alertness of your mind
SIX—relax your body as you move deeper
FIVE—approach the center of your knowing
FOUR—move into your center
THREE—remember that you do *know*
TWO—notice *how* you know
ONE—*experience* your crystal clarity

Remember that you are one who knows many things. You do understand what is true for you, and you can express your understanding.

You can begin by *seeing* what you know. Notice the random images that are rolling through your consciousness now. Pay attention to the shapes, designs, and colors as you let the pictures slide by. See the light and dark parts, the soft and bold parts. Remember that you can often see what you know. (Pause)

You can also *hear* what you know. Listen carefully for any sounds that flow through you. Notice if they are the sounds of nature or of people. Mentally adjust the volume if you need to and tune in to the music or words. Allow the sounds to float away as you remember that you can often hear what you know. (Pause)

And, you can *feel* what you know. Notice sensations in your body that help you keep yourself comfortable and relaxed. Become aware of emotions that briefly touch you and move on. Sense the texture and shape of your emotions, their softness and hardness. Hold each sensation for a moment and let it slip away. Remember that you can often feel what you know.

As you continue to remember your knowing, allow your attention to become more focused within your consciousness. Allow your mind to be alert and awake while your body continues to relax. And, bring your mind and your awareness to the tarot. Think about the tarot deck and allow your attention to come to rest with the [*NAME OF THE CARD*].

.   .   .   .

As you focus on the [*NAME OF THE CARD*] imagine your own card.
Remember that you can *see* what you know about this card—
Colors...Shapes...Designs...Pictures...A Story Unfolding

You can also *hear* what you know about the [*NAME OF THE CARD*]—
Sounds...Words...Birds and Animals...Natural Forces...Music

And, you can *feel* what you know about the card—
Physical Sensations...Body Positions...Feelings...Emotions.

Notice everything you can about your [*NAME OF THE CARD*] and hold it in your consciousness. As you remember your card, calmly open your eyes and write or draw everything you know about your [*NAME OF THE CARD*].

(Repeat the process with more cards, starting with [*NAME OF THE CARD*], or move on out.)

Now that you've discovered what you know about this (these) card(s), close your eyes and relax into your center once more. Thank yourself for remembering what you know. Appreciate who you are and the strength of your awareness. And, gradually, as you are ready, come back to your usual consciousness and open your eyes again.

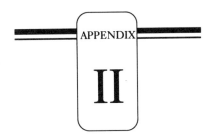

Symbol Glossary

1. Tarot Suits

As we discussed in chapter 4, the four suits in the Minor Arcana are associated with the four elements of our world. Similar to the principle that the three primary colors—red, blue and yellow—make up the basis of all other color, so it is true that the four elements; fire, water, air, and earth are the basis to which all biological forms interact. The kind of energy an element possesses is symbolized with a correlating suit. Remember that suits (element) represent a specific area of our lives. All cards with the same suit will have a consistent meaning related to that suit.

Suit	Symbol	Correspondences
Wands		Element: Fire, Active Energy, Identity & Ego, Creative Energy, Growth and Awareness of the Self.
Cups		Element: Water, Receptive Energy, Unconscious Awareness, Intuition, Emotions, Relationships.
Swords		Element: Air, Mental Energy, Conscious Mind, Philosophical Values, Communication.
Pentacles		Element: Earth, Groundedness, Material Values, Physical Manifestations, Tangible World.

2. Tarot Numbers

In the Minor Arcana numbers are used as symbols to help recall the nature of a particular behavior, feeling, attitude or event. They do not indicate an amount of something. Rather, they suggest that the nature within the area of life the suit is signifying—such as the mental or emotional arena—is stimulating or stagnating, beginning or repeating the same pattern, or whatever else the correlating number might represent. Below is a list of the numbers One (Ace) through Ten and their meanings. To better understand the qualities on the rest of the Minor Arcana—the Court cards; the Page, Knight, Queen and King, refer to the Court cards and the Tree of Life section at the end of Appendix II (page 187).

Card Number	Card Meaning
1	Point of beginning.
2	Balance, harmony, affirming, deciding, duality, reflection.
3	Planning, projecting, triangle, "creating ideas."
4	Stability, manifestation, order with definite boundaries.
5	Challenge, adversity or destruction which necessitates change, adaptation.
6	Harmonious patterning; a physical coming together; expansive rhythm, two triangles (2 x 3) which depict the coming together of Above and Below.
7	Accomplishments on inner planes; self-expansion, imagination, evaluation through experimentation.
8	Organizing, structuring, systems, limiting; inspiration, desire for order (balance), definition.
9	Integration of concepts; trinity of trinities; center (purpose) and direction for processing (physical) action.
10	Successful completion; waiting for transition to something new; transformation.

3. Planetary Symbols

The symbols of the planets are used in astrology to represent a kind of active energy. They show the personality functions and urges that are manifested by a person. Planetary symbols are often used in tarot by those who wish to relate the card to astrological symbolism. For some, it serves as another tool in expanding the interpretation of a card. Basic planetary functions are:

Planet	Symbol	Function
MOON	☽	to use emotional habit patterns, to create emotional security.
MERCURY	☿	to think logically, to learn new things, to be curious.
VENUS	♀	to find value and attract things of value to create beauty.
SUN	☉	to illuminate things, to maximize personal potential and growth.
MARS	♂	to be aggressive, to pursue desires, to take initiative.
JUPITER	♃	to expand, to get "more," to philosophize, to teach.
SATURN	♄	to organize, to structure, to discipline, to conserve.
CHIRON	⚷	to manifest the ideal into the real, to solve problems.
URANUS	♅	to rebel, to be eccentric or unique, to be progressive.
NEPTUNE	♆	to dissolve barriers, to release boundaries, to be psychic.
PLUTO	♇	to transform things slowly, to destroy and reconstruct.
EARTH	⊕	Astrological symbol which depicts two halves, (duality/polarity) made into four quarters—the root of all quadrate things on earth such as the four seasons, the four elements or the four corners of the earth; manifestation, physical, material realm.

4. Astrological Signs

Astrological signs symbolize twelve distinct approaches to life. Each sign reflects a different style or way of being. A sign is pictorial, (*i.e.*, Ram for Aries, or the Lion for Leo) and represent various psychological needs and attitudes through which people experience life.

In tarot, some have chosen to use astrological symbols in order to give further insight as to the nature of the card. Astrological signs can act as yet one more reference of association for the "energy" of the card.

Astrological Sign	Astrological Symbol	Correspondences
Aries	♈	Late March to late April. Symbol: the Ram. Colors: red, scarlet. Key-word Phrase: I am. Traits: independent, pioneering, adventuresome, pushy.
Taurus	♉	Late April to late May. Symbol: the Bull. Colors: pink, rose (earth tones). Key-word Phrase: I have. Traits: resourceful, practical, result-oriented, stubborn.
Gemini	♊	Late May to late June. Symbol: the Twins. Colors: yellow, silver. Key-word Phrase: I think. Traits: mentally quick, stimulating, versatile, flexible, undependable.
Cancer	♋	Late June to late July. Symbol: the Crab. Colors: gray, silver, white and sea-green. Key-word Phrase: I feel. Traits: emotional, comforting, nurturing, "belonged," clingy.
Leo	♌	Late July to late August. Symbol: the Lion. Colors: gold, purple, orange, yellow. Key-word Phrase: I will. Traits: shining, self-expressive, magnanimous, attention-getting.
Virgo	♍	Late August to late September. Symbol: the Virgin. Colors: navy, gray, earth-brown. Key-word Phrase: I analyze. Traits: analytical, problem-solving, detail-oriented, precise, picky.
Libra	♎	Late September to late October. Symbol: the Scales (balance). Colors: blue-green, light blue. Key-word Phrase: I Balance. Traits: cooperative, fair-minded, balanced, diplomatic, indecisive.

Astrological Sign	Astrological Symbol	Correspondences
Scorpio	♏	Late October to late November. Symbol: the Scorpion or the Eagle. Colors: red, black, deep maroon, crimson. Key-word Phrase: I focus. Traits: focused, intense, self-protective, committed, defensive.
Sagittarius	♐	Late November to late December. Symbol: the Archer. Colors: purple, green, turquoise. Key-word Phrase: I know. Traits: philosophical, expansive, growth-oriented, free, self-indulgent.
Capricorn	♑	Late December to late January. Symbol: the Goat. Colors: black, gray. Key-word Phrase: I use. Traits: conservative, responsible, ambitious, constructive, restrictive.
Aquarius	♒	Late January to late February. Symbol: the Cup-bearer. Colors: checks, stripes, blue. Key-word Phrase: I envision. Traits: inventive, non-conforming, future-oriented, rebellious.
Pisces	♓	Late February to late March. Symbol: the Fish. Colors: lavender, violet, sea-green, white. Key-word Phrase: I believe. Traits: compassionate, spiritual, healing, psychic, self-sacrificing.

5. The Tree of Life

The Tree of Life is a graph-like system of interconnected spheres and pathways that depict the various developmental phases of life, from God or the Source (the Absolute) to Matter (Manifestation). See figure 5 on page 188. It is associated with Tarot because of the relationship that occurs between the Major Arcana and the pathways (the lines between the spheres on the Tree diagram), and the Minor Arcana which are identified on the Tree of Life with the spheres or Sephiroth (singular Sephira). Also, the four sections or forces of matter described on the Tree are seen as the four suits of tarot: Wands are Fire, Cups are Water, Swords are Air, and Pentacles are Earth.

On the Tree as in tarot, the pathways, (Major Arcana) are viewed as the subjective forces of human experiences, whereas the Minor Ar-

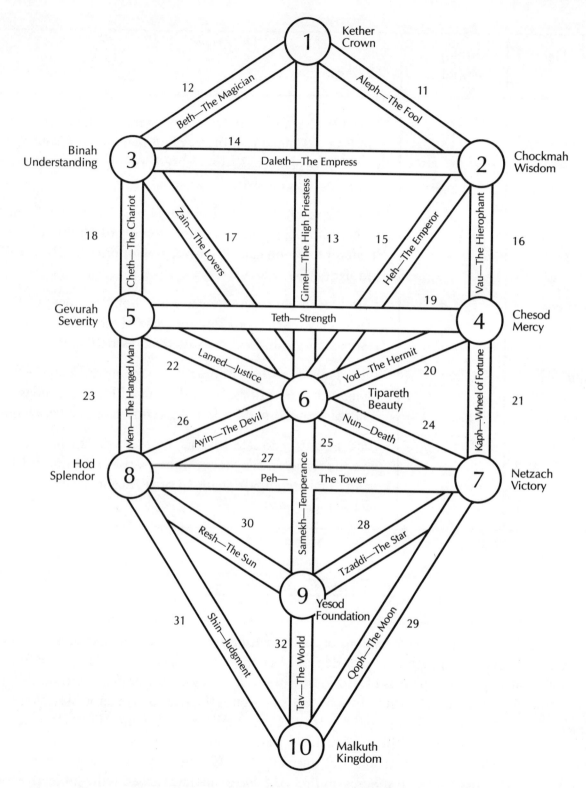

Figure 5. The Tree of Life graph, Sephiroth and path indications.

cana, equated with the Sephiroth (spheres), are considered to represent the objective occurrences of everyday existence.

A significant correlation does exist between the Tree of Life and tarot. Some believe that a thorough study of the Tree will enhance one's understanding of the tarot. However, it is an individual interest and not necessarily a requirement to comprehending tarot, that will lead you to investigate the Tree of Life further. If you are interested in doing so, *Introduction to the Golden Dawn Tarot*, or *Qabalistic Tarot* by Robert Wang (published by Samuel Weiser, Inc.) is an excellent reference. Another is *A Practical Guide to Qabalistic Symbolism*, by Gareth Knight (Samuel Weiser). These and other books are listed in Suggested Reading.

To follow is a brief explanation of the Sephiroth on the Tree of Life. Compare the attributes of a particular sephira with the attributes of the same number on the Minor Arcana. See Tarot Numbers on page 184; in the beginning of Appendix II for easy reference.

Sephiroth on the Tree of Life

Placement of the Sephiroth	Symbol	Attribution	Minor Arcana
1 Kether/Crown		Emanation from the Absolute Light of the Beginning	Ace/1
2 Chockmah/Wisdom		Emanation of life-force. Masculine aspect; creative principle; the stimulation which precedes action; Great Father.	Two
3 Binah/Understanding		Emanation of faith. Feminine aspect of creative principle. Receptivity at the point of action. Where one becomes many; Great Mother.	Three
4 Chesod/Mercy (Kindness)		Receiving intelligence (awareness); power point of action. Cosmic foundation; framework for manifestation.	Four

Sephiroth on the Tree of Life (cont.)

Placement of the Sephiroth	Symbol	Attribution	Minor Arcana
5 Gevurah/Severity		Cosmic justice. Adversity when opposing Divine Law. Success or failure as a result of being in or out of accordance with Divine Law. Clarity; courage.	Five
6 Tipareth/Beauty (Sun/Center)		Beauty from harmony. Balance point as a result of the power from Above (Heaven) coming together with the power from Below (Earth). Christ energy; healing; redemption.	Six
7 Netzach/Victory		Hidden intelligence (awareness). Intellectual virtues; definite accomplishment through right desires; love; feelings; instincts.	Seven
8 Hod/Splendor		Perfect intelligence (awareness). First stages of illumination. Balance with desire; reason.	Eight
9 Yesod/Foundation		Fundamental power. Point where higher consciousness transforms into lower consciousness. Plane just above physical (ethereal, psychic, astral). Guidance from Above to physical is through this plane.	Nine
10 Malkuth/Kingdom		Perfect manifestation. Final phase of creation of cosmic forces on physical plane. The sphere to which creation is complete. The point where concept must begin "anew." Involution—evolution. Kether below.	Ten

6. Paths on the Tree of Life

To begin to see the correlation of qualities between the Major Arcana cards in the tarot and the various Paths on the Tree of Life, view the interpretations that we have given in the journal and sketchbook section of the *Workbook* for each card title under the tarot heading in this chart. Compare it with the description under the title of the Path Number/Name listed here. For example, when you look up THE FOOL in the journal section, you'll find that it is regarded, among other things, as the card of pure potential. Here you will see that ALEPH is considered as the path of the Undeveloped potential of all. Note that the first Path on the Tree starts with number 11 because it follows number 10—the last Sephira on the glyph.

Paths on the Tree of Life

Path Number/Name	Path	Name	Attribute	Number/Title Major Arcana
11 **ALEPH** Kether (Crown) to Chockmah (Wisdom)		Crown + Wisdom = ALEPH	Absolute + *Life Force* = Undeveloped potential of ALL. Potential in pure form.	**0** **THE FOOL**
12 **BETH** Kether (Crown) to Binah (Understanding)		Crown + Understanding = BETH	Absolute + *Faith* = Initial existence of a point. "Something from nothing." "The mind of the universe."	**I** **MAGICIAN**

Paths on the Tree of Life (cont.)

Path Number/Name	Path	Name	Attribute	Number/Title Major Arcana
13 GIMEL Kether (Crown) to Tipareth (Sun/Beauty)		Crown + Beauty = GIMEL	Absolute + *Balance* = Pathway between God (above) and manifestation (below). Spiritual unity.	**II HIGH PRIESTESS**
14 DALETH Chockmah (Wisdom) to Binah (Understanding)		Wisdom + Understanding = DALETH	Life Force + *Faith* = Illuminated intelligence. Source of holiness. Initiation of creative receptivity.	**III EMPRESS**
15 HEH Chockmah (Wisdom) to Tipareth (Sun/Beauty)		Wisdom + Beauty = HEH	Life Force + *Harmony* = Activation of energy. Link between creative principle and "active," physical. The initiation of matter.	**IV EMPEROR**

Paths on the Tree of Life (cont.)

Path Number/Name	Path	Name	Attribute	Number/Title Major Arcana
16 VAU Chockmah (Wisdom) to Chesod (Mercy)		Wisdom + Mercy = VAU	Life Force + *Divine Will* = Receiving intelligence (love principle). Spiritual awareness and guidance.	**V** **HIEROPHANT** (Teacher)
17 ZAIN Binah (Understanding) to Tipareth (Beauty)		Understanding + Beauty = ZAIN	Faith + *Harmony* = Law of attraction. Receptive creative principle transformed into active (manifesting) principle. Physical union (yin/yang). The coming together of contrary qualities for a third principle = law of attraction.	**VI** **THE** **LOVERS**

Paths on the Tree of Life (cont.)

Path Number/Name	Path	Name	Attribute	Number/Title Major Arcana
18 CHETH Binah (Understanding) to Chesod (Mercy)		Understanding + Severity = CHETH	Faith + *Divine Justice* = Natural order. Receptive creative principle trans- formed into cos- mic law. An es- tablishment of controlled action.	**VII CHARIOT**
19 TETH Gevurah (Severity) to Chesod (Mercy)		Severity + Mercy = TETH	Divine Justice + *Divine Will* = Law of action. The discipline achieved from the relationship of bal- anced active (male) force with receptive (female) nature. Archetypal matriarchal con- sciousness.	**VIII STRENGTH**

Paths on the Tree of Life (cont.)

Path Number/Name	Path	Name	Attribute	Number/Title Major Arcana
20 YOD Chesod (Mercy) to Tipareth (Beauty)		Mercy + Beauty = YOD	Divine Will + *Harmony* = Balanced will. Receptive intelligence transformed through the balance point of above/below creating will guided by wisdom. Prophetic wisdom.	**IX HERMIT**
21 KAPH Chesod (Mercy) to Netzach (Victory)		Mercy + Victory = KAPH	Divine Will + *Accomplishment* = Reward. Receiving intelligence (of divine influence) together with accomplishment transforms into the reactive and cyclic forces of life. "What goes around comes around."	**X WHEEL OF FORTUNE**
22 LAMED Gevurah (Severity) to Tipareth (Beauty)		Severity + Beauty = LAMED	Divine Justice + *Harmony* = The Law of Cause and Effect (karma). The balance between the law of nature (or justice) and the gateway of love and matter (above/below) creates cause and effect.	**XI JUSTICE**

Paths on the Tree of Life (cont.)

Path Number/Name	Path	Name	Attribute	Number/Title Major Arcana
23 MEM Gevurah (Severity) to Hod (Splendor)		Severity + Splendor = MEM	Divine Justice + *Illumination* = Foundation of perma- nent existence (aware- ness of Spirit). The awareness of self-limi- tation on a lower level with unlimited free- dom on a higher level.	**XII** **HANGED** **MAN** (Suspended One)
24 NUN Tipareth (Sun/Beauty) to Netzach (Victory)		Beauty + Victory = NUN	Harmony + *Victory* = Change. The center point of harmony (the gateway between above & below) to- gether with trium- phant victory (self-ex- pansion) creates change.	**XIII** **DEATH** (Transformation)

Paths on the Tree of Life (cont.)

Path Number/Name	Path	Name	Attribute	Number/Title Major Arcana
25 SAMEKH Tipareth (Beauty) to Yesod (Foundation)		Beauty + Foundation = SAMEKH	Harmony + *Fundamental Power* = Stabilization of consciousness. The gateway (or "harmonious" point of above/below) together with the power point (the point where higher consciousness transforms into lower consciousness) just above physical, creates the stabilization of consciousness. Consciousness fusing with light creates stable awareness.	**XIV** **TEMPERANCE**
26 AYIN Tipareth (Beauty) to Hod (Splendor)		Beauty + Splendor = AYIN	Harmony + *Balance of Desire* = Opportunity for spiritual unfoldment or denial. The central point or gateway of above & below combined with the energy of the balance point of desire (or the lack of balance point) creates the opportunity for illumination, or for the shadow and veil of ignorance.	**XV** **THE DEVIL** (The Adversary)

Paths on the Tree of Life (cont.)

Path Number/Name	Path	Name	Attribute	Number/Title Major Arcana
27 **PEH** Hod (Splendor) to Netzach (Victory)		Splendor + Victory = PEH	Balance of Desire + *Accomplishment* = Truth. Enlightenment results when self-delusion (i.e., the "state of imbalanced desire") is shattered and truth remains.	**XVI** **TOWER**
28 **TZADDI** Netzach (Victory) to Yesod (Foundation)		Victory + Foundation = TZADDI	Accomplishment + *Fundamental Power* = Active intelligence. Healing power that comes from illumination. Infinite energy; infinite intelligence.	**XVII** **THE STAR**
29 **QOPH** Netzach (Victory) to Malkuth (Kingdom)		Victory + Kingdom = QOPH	Accomplishment + *Manifestation* = Physical Consciousness. Reflection of triumphant accomplishment (or lack of) together with physical awareness creates the "state of unconscious desires (vision of triumph accomplishment) or fears (vision of defeat).	**XVIII** **THE MOON**

Paths on the Tree of Life (cont.)

Path Number/Name	Path	Name	Attribute	Number/Title Major Arcana
30 RESH Hod (Splendor) to Yesod (Foundation)		Splendor + Foundation = RESH	Balance of Desire + *Fundamental Power* = Collective Awareness. "Living" intelligence. The balance of desire together with fundamental power creates regeneration of conscious/subconscious awareness of the "whole." A revitalization and expansion of consciousness.	**XIX** **THE SUN**
31 SHIN Hod (Splendor) to Malkuth (Kingdom)		Splendor + Kingdom = SHIN	Balance of Desire + *Manifestation* = Awareness and acceptance of Self. Divine judgment (which is forgiveness and acceptance of Self). Resurrection.	**XX** **JUDGMENT** (Aeon, etc.)
32 TAV Yesod (Foundation) to Malkuth (Kingdom)		Foundation + Kingdom = TAV	Fundamental Power + *Manifestation* = Completion of creation. Fundamental power (the point where higher consciousness transforms into lower consciousness) together with perfect manifestation creates guiding intelligence and cosmic consciousness which is the union of the individual body and the Spirit of All.	**XXI** **THE WORLD** (The Universe) (The Cosmos)

7. The Court Cards and the Tree of Life

Each of the four Court cards in a tarot deck is positioned on the Sephira (sphere) that correlates with the qualities it symbolizes. Until recently the most common titles of the four Court cards were the King, Queen, Prince (or Knight) and Princess. Today there are many decks that publish court cards with other names, *i.e.*, Shaman, Priestess, Son, Daughter, etc. Whatever the title, the important thing to remember is that the image or symbol that is used is a suggestion for the basic *principle* it represents. It is not the intention that a particular court card be interpreted as an image for a certain personality type or stereotypical idea relating only to a specific gender or role. Kings, for instance represent completion and outgoing or active energy, and are positioned on the second Sephira (Chockmah). The principle symbolized by Chockmah is the Great Father or masculine aspect (outgoing or active energy). It is creativity in its stimulated or before-action form.

In all, there are four "Pillars" on the Tree of Life (see figure 6 on page 202). *Chockmah* is associated with *Kings* and represents the principle described above. *Queens* are *Binah*, the Great Mother who receives the energy of Chockmah and initiates it into action. *Knights* are *Tipareth*, which is in the center of the Tree and represents the Christ Energy or the point where the power of the Absolute (Kether) is "brought down" for the purpose of manifesting matter. And *Malkuth*, which is associated with the *Page*, is Earth. It is the final stage of creation and is both the completion point and returning point of "The Beginning" (Absolute).

If you are interested in furthering your understanding of the Four Worlds of the Tree of Life and their relationship to tarot, see *Qabalistic Tarot* by Robert Wang (Samuel Weiser, Inc.) or any of the other Qabalah books listed in the Suggested Reading section.

CHOCKMAH

TAROT PERSONIFICATION—KING, SHAMAN, ETC.
TAROT SUIT SYMBOL—WAND
SPIRITUAL ELEMENT—PRIMAL FIRE
WORLD (ASPECT)—ARCHETYPAL/SPIRIT
ATTRIBUTES—GREAT FATHER, DYNAMIC ENERGY, ACTIVE

BINAH

TAROT PERSONIFICATION—QUEEN, PRIESTESS, ETC.
TAROT SUIT SYMBOL—CUPS

SPIRITUAL ELEMENT—PRIMAL WATER
WORLD (ASPECT)—CREATIVE/UNCONSCIOUS
ATTRIBUTES—GREAT MOTHER, RECEPTIVE ENERGY

TIPARETH

TAROT PERSONIFICATION—PRINCE, PAGE, SON, KNIGHT, ETC.
TAROT SUIT SYMBOL—SWORDS
SPIRITUAL ELEMENT—PRIMAL AIR
WORLD (ASPECT)—FORMATIVE/SUBCONSCIOUS
ATTRIBUTES—HARMONY, TRANSFORMATION OF ABOVE TO BELOW

MALKUTH

TAROT PERSONIFICATION—PRINCESS, DAUGHTER, ETC.
TAROT SUIT SYMBOL—PENTACLES, COINS, DISCS, ETC.
SPIRITUAL ELEMENT—PRIMAL EARTH
WORLD (ASPECT)—ACTIVE/CONSCIOUS
ATTRIBUTES—COMPLETION OF CREATION, MANIFESTATION

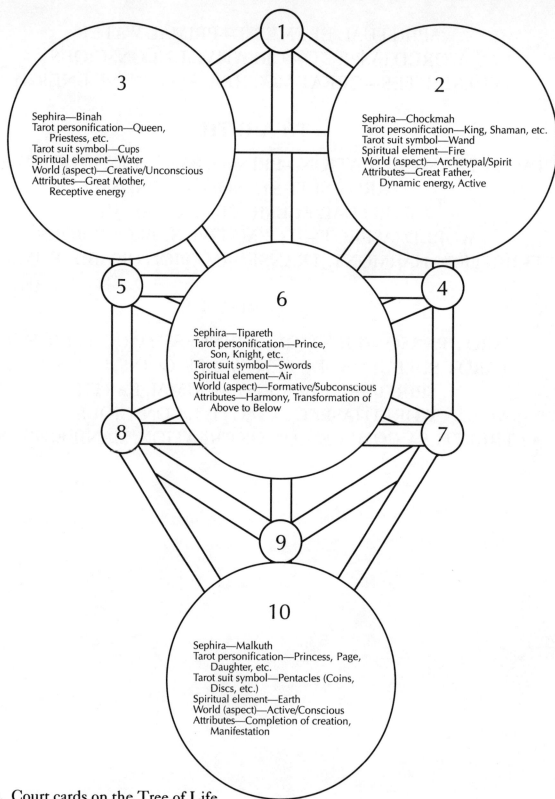

3

Sephira—Binah
Tarot personification—Queen,
    Priestess, etc.
Tarot suit symbol—Cups
Spiritual element—Water
World (aspect)—Creative/Unconscious
Attributes—Great Mother,
    Receptive energy

2

Sephira—Chockmah
Tarot personification—King, Shaman, etc.
Tarot suit symbol—Wand
Spiritual element—Fire
World (aspect)—Archetypal/Spirit
Attributes—Great Father,
    Dynamic energy, Active

6

Sephira—Tipareth
Tarot personification—Prince,
    Son, Knight, etc.
Tarot suit symbol—Swords
Spiritual element—Air
World (aspect)—Formative/Subconscious
Attributes—Harmony, Transformation of
    Above to Below

10

Sephira—Malkuth
Tarot personification—Princess, Page,
    Daughter, etc.
Tarot suit symbol—Pentacles (Coins,
    Discs, etc.)
Spiritual element—Earth
World (aspect)—Active/Conscious
Attributes—Completion of creation,
    Manifestation

Figure 6. Court cards on the Tree of Life

Suggested Reading

For further information on the tarot:

Arrien, Angeles. *The Tarot Handbook.* Sonoma, CA: Arcus Publishing Co., 1984.

Butler, Bill. *Dictionary of Tarot.* New York: Schocken Books, l975.

Fairfield, Gail. *Choice Centered Tarot.* Seattle, WA: Ramp Creek Publishing, 1981, 1989,

Gearhart, Sally. *A Feminist Tarot.* (revised and expanded edition) Watertown, MA: Persephone Press, 1981.

Greer, Mary. *Tarot Constellations: Patterns of Personal Destiny.* North Hollywood, CA: Newcastle Publishing, 1984.

———. *Tarot For Your Self.* North Hollywood, CA: Newcastle Publishing, 1984.

———. *Tarot Mirrors: Reflections of Personal Meaning.* North Hollywood, CA: Newcastle Publishing, 1988.

Jung, C.G. *Memories, Dreams and Reflections.* New York: Vintage Books, 1961.

Kaplan, Stuart. *The Encyclopedia of Tarot. Vol. 1.* Stamford, CT: U.S. Games Systems, 1978; *The Encyclopedia of Tarot, Vol. 2,* 1985; *The Encyclopedia of Tarot, Vol. 3,* 1990.

Nichols, Sallie. *Jung and Tarot: an Archetypal Journey.* York Beach, ME: Samuel Weiser, Inc., 1980.

Noble, Vicki. *Motherpeace: A Way to the Goddess Through Myth, Art and Tarot.* San Francisco: HarperCollins, 1983.

Wanless, James. *Voyager Tarot: Way of the Great Oracle.* Carmel, CA: Merrill-West, 1989.

For further information on the qabalah:

Knight, Gareth. *A Practical Guide to Qabalistic Symbolism.* (Volumes I and II in one edition.) York Beach, ME: Samuel Weiser, 1978.

Roberts, Richard and Joseph Campbell. *Tarot Revelations*. San Fransisco: Vernal Equinox, 1979.

Wang, Robert. *Introduction to the Golden Dawn Tarot*. York Beach, ME: Samuel Weiser, 1978.

———. *Qabalistic Tarot*. York Beach, ME: Samuel Weiser, 1987.

Some ideas for cultivating your creativity:

Edwards, Betty. *Drawing On the Artist Within*. New York: Simon & Schuster, 1986.

———. *Drawing on the Right Side of the Brain*. Los Angeles: J.P. Tarcher, 1979.

Garfield, Patricia. *Creative Dreaming*. New York: Random House, 1976.

Gawain, Shatki. *Creative Visualization*. Mill Valley, CA: Whatever Publishing, 1978.

McMurray, Madeline. *Illuminations: The Healing Image*. Berkeley, CA: Wingbow Press, 1989.

Mariechild, Diane. *Mother Wit: A Feminist Guide to Psychic Development: Exercises for Healing, Growth, and Spiritual Awareness*. Freedom, CA: The Crossing Press, 1981.

Rainer, Tristine. *The New Diary: How to Use a Journal for Self-Guidance and Expanded Creativity*. Los Angeles: J.P. Tarcher, 1978.

Starhawk. *The Spiral Dance: A Rebirth of Ancient Religion of the Great Goddess*. New York: HarperCollins, 1979.

More on rituals and meditation techniques:

Budapest, Z. *Grandmother of Time: A Women's Book of Celebrations, Spells and Sacred Objects for Every Month of the Year*. New York: HarperCollins, 1989.

Greer, Mary. *The Audio Exploration of Tarot: Meditations and Rituals*. Los Angeles, CA: Audio Renaissance Tapes, 1988.

Parrish-Harra, Carol. *Book of Rituals: Keys to Planetary Transformation*. Santa Monica, CA: IBS Press, 1991.

Walker, Barbara G. *Women's Rituals*. New York: HarperCollins, 1990.

Photo by Jeff Gering.

Gail Fairfield writes and teaches astrology and tarot, as well as working with NLP with her many students. She is the author of *Choice Centered Tarot* and *Choice Centered Astrology*. Gail runs *Choice Centered* seminars around the United States.

Patti Provo met Gail Fairfield in 1987 to work on this project. Patti is a freelance writer and is presently taking courses at the University of Washington. She is currently involved in giving lectures and workshops that enlarge upon the concepts in *Inspiration Tarot*.

NAMES FOR THE CARD

Traditional: _____

Alternatives: _____

_____

My Choice: _____

_____

SYMBOLS

Tree of Life Path: _____

Astrological Sign: _____

Astrological Planet: _____

Colors: _____

Mine: _____

_____

_____

INTERPRETATIONS

_____

_____

_____

_____

_____

_____

_____

_____

_____

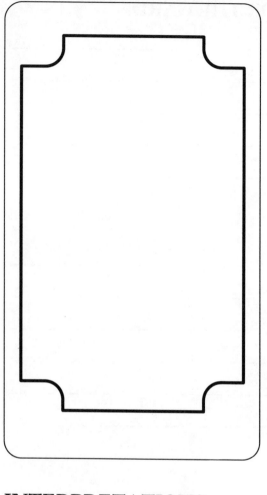

NAMES FOR THE CARD

Traditional: _____

Alternatives: _____

_____

My Choice: _____

_____

SYMBOLS

Tree of Life Path: _____

Astrological Sign: _____

Astrological Planet: _____

Colors: _____

Mine: _____

_____

_____

INTERPRETATIONS

_____

_____

_____

_____

_____

_____

_____

_____

NAMES FOR THE CARD

Traditional: _____

Alternatives: _____

_____

My Choice: _____

_____

SYMBOLS

Tree of Life Path: _____

Astrological Sign: _____

Astrological Planet: _____

Colors: _____

Mine: _____

_____

_____

INTERPRETATIONS

_____

_____

_____

_____

_____

_____

_____

_____

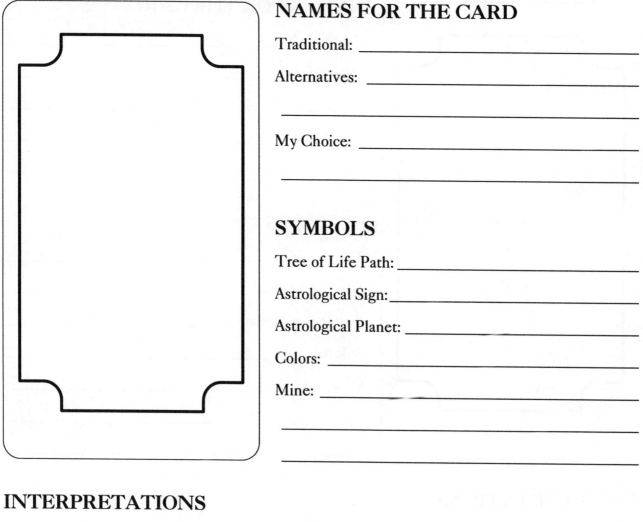

NAMES FOR THE CARD

Traditional: _____

Alternatives: _____

_____

My Choice: _____

_____

SYMBOLS

Tree of Life Path: _____

Astrological Sign: _____

Astrological Planet: _____

Colors: _____

Mine: _____

_____

_____

INTERPRETATIONS

_____

_____

_____

_____

_____

_____

_____

_____

NAMES FOR THE CARD

Traditional: _____

Alternatives: _____

_____

My Choice: _____

_____

SYMBOLS

Tree of Life Path: _____

Astrological Sign: _____

Astrological Planet: _____

Colors: _____

Mine: _____

_____

_____

INTERPRETATIONS

_____

_____

_____

_____

_____

_____

_____

_____

_____

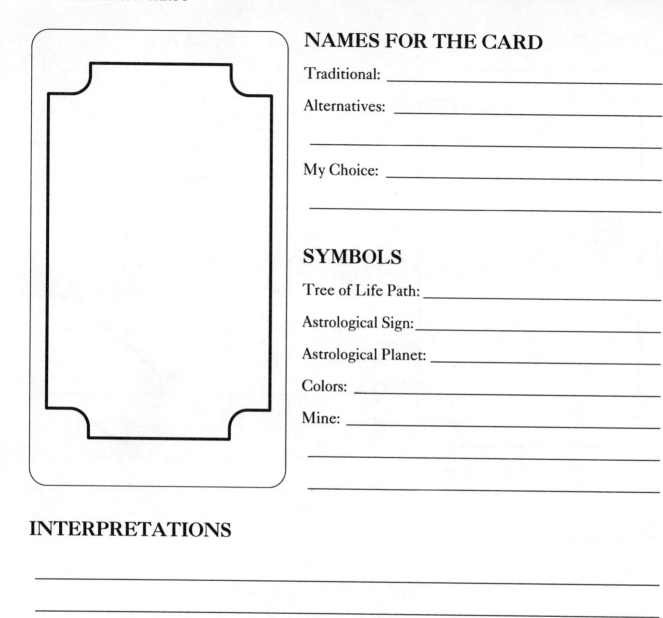

NAMES FOR THE CARD

Traditional: _____

Alternatives: _____

_____

My Choice: _____

_____

SYMBOLS

Tree of Life Path: _____

Astrological Sign: _____

Astrological Planet: _____

Colors: _____

Mine: _____

_____

_____

INTERPRETATIONS

_____

_____

_____

_____

_____

_____

_____

_____